The Herb Garden Club

A Collection of Herbal Stories and Activities for Children of All Ages

Kathy Stevens

Illustrated by
Nyssa Shaw

Contents

Contents, cont'd

The Weed Bucket

When I was young, my parents planted a vegetable garden in our backyard. I remember the stately artichoke bush and bright red tomatoes waiting to be picked. There were fruit trees, shrubs, and colorful flowers. It was my job to pull weeds. Mom or Dad would hand me a bucket and tell me to fill it to the very top with weeds. I would look inside that big bucket and wonder. . . how long is this going to take?

I'm not sure how many times that bucket was filled. Though I learned to pull those weeds in record time, it was never fun.

Fast-forward twelve years. In my twenties, I loved to visit nurseries. Roaming the aisles of those green havens, I filled the shopping cart with lots of flowers, vegetables and herbs along with an occasional shrub or tree. My home had a flower garden planted next to the front door. Pansies, snapdragons, and daisies enjoyed a crisp spring morning. I, too, had an artichoke plant in my backyard. Flowering shrubs framed the front yard. It surprised me how much I loved growing things. Filling the weed bucket was no longer a chore. It gave me quiet time to be with the plants, watching them grow and change over time.

I rarely put on a pair of gardening gloves because my hands want to touch the chocolate brown earth. While digging a hole for a tomato plant, I am surrounded by sunshine, blue sky, and fresh air. Butterflies, ladybugs, toads, and tree frogs are never far away. I once read an anonymous quote, "nature is my nature." So many times those words have echoed through my mind as I work in the garden. Perhaps more than any other place I go, the garden is where I am most at home with myself.

As the years went by, I planted herbs, lots of them. I planted them alongside flowers, vegetables, and beneath trees. In the beginning, lavender was my favorite and I planted several species of this sweet smelling herb. Then I discovered rosemary, thyme, lemon balm; the list goes on. There are so many ways to use them. I began by making lavender cookies and lemon balm tea. Before long they were being sprinkled in salads and tucked between the pages of my favorite books. Purchasing herb books and journals became one of my passions. I simply had to learn everything possible about these amazing plants. Before I knew it, herbs were woven into every part of my life.

Creating a garden at the elementary school where I taught 4th grade was a way I could share herbs and gardening with my students. I hoped the students would love the garden and visit it often. Lots of them did and still do. Over the years they have joined me during their morning recess to weed and plant. Parent volunteers have also come to lend a hand.

Little did I know this garden would continue to thrive twenty years later. That it would become an inspiration for an herb garden club and for home gardens. When it was time for me to retire from teaching, I simply could not say good by to the garden. I promised students, teachers and my former principal that I would continue to care for the garden and host a garden club.

It has been said that children in today's world have a nature deficit. In *Last Child In The Woods*, Richard Louv writes about how little time children spend with nature. Television, computers, instant messaging, and Nintendo have often taken away their outdoor playtime. Mr. Louv has many great ideas about how to address this deficit and one of them is growing a school or family garden.

I know that the Crestwood School garden is a place where children spend time with nature every day. Looking, listening, smelling, touching, and sometimes tasting, our garden is an engaging place to be. When students plant marigolds alongside the stepping stones or discover a hummingbird visiting the butterfly bush, they are communing with nature. Change is a constant in the garden. Every morning, before the bell rings, I encourage students to walk the garden, looking for anything that is different from the day before. They are thrilled to see a sparkling new spider web glistening in the sunlight or a lemon balm sprout growing alongside the mother plant. What a spectacular way to begin the school day!

Looking back on my childhood, I am glad my parents handed me a weed bucket.

Say Hello to William!

William is a robin. He's also a Protector of the garden. His job is to stop insects from eating precious flowers. He enjoys singing, sharing news with other birds and spending time with the children you'll read about in this book.

You might see William in your own garden. Robins have bright red chests, yellow beaks, and black or brown bodies. If you see a robin taking an interest in your herb garden, it might be William.

To learn more about William, or the recipes or stories in this book, visit www.timelessherbaltraditions.com.

A WORD OF CAUTION FROM WILLIAM

Many of the recipes in this book have to be made in a kitchen, where the use of an oven, stove, blender, knife, or other kitchen tools may be used. We recommend that all of the recipes in this book be made with adult supervision.

Two of the recipes in this book are made with honey. Children under the age of two should not consume honey.

A Few Words About the Crestwood Garden

In 1995, my fourth grade class and I decided to plant a garden. We planned to put herbs, flowers, shrubs, and vegetables in our garden. Our first task was to create a place for the garden. Just outside our classroom was a large rectangular area filled with decomposed granite. We knew it would be a perfect location. The decomposed granite was removed and a truckload of soil came to take its place. Sprinklers were installed for irrigation.

To pay for this endeavor, all three fourth grade classes and their families cleaned out cupboards and closets. A yard sale was held in front of the school office. The money earned easily paid for the sprinklers and the exchange of granite for topsoil. We also purchased twelve-inch red pavers to build a walkway through the garden.

The first year we experimented with different garden designs. After watching children work and play in the garden, I joined with parents and students to create a meandering pathway that winds across the length of the garden.

Many students still walk this pathway every day, stopping to smell a rose, freshen their breath with a sprig of mint, or pick a lamb's ear to pet or use as a bookmark.

During those years as a classroom teacher, my students and I enjoyed as many garden moments as possible. We made herbal teas and waters. We added dried or fresh herbs to soup, breads, and pasta salad. In addition, the garden provided inspiration for math and science lessons, poetry, creative writing, and watercolor painting.

In 2010, I retired from teaching and started the Herb Garden Club. We meet once a week after school to learn about the herbs growing in our garden. Though no longer a classroom teacher, I continue to care for the herb garden with Crestwood students. They join me one day a week during their morning recess. There are weeds to pull, herbs and flowers to plant, and shrubs that need pruning. When the recess bell rings, calling them back to class, they reluctantly put their garden tools away.

An Invitation to Join the Herb Garden Club

The Herb Garden Club meets at 2:15 on Wednesday afternoons, in the library at Crestwood Elementary School. We collect our supplies, decide on a plan for the day, and head into the sweet-scented garden across the courtyard. In our garden, we grow thirty herbs for cooking, medicine, or creating perfume.

To take part in our club, you will need:

A journal for garden notes (pick whatever journal you like the best);

A pencil box filled with colored markers, a glue stick, and a pencil;

A camera (optional).

You'll fill your journal with this week's herb notes starting from "Lavender" in Chapter one. If you like, you can draw colorful borders around your weekly entry. You can sketch simple pictures of the leaves, bumblebees, hummingbirds, or butterflies you see in the garden. You can even glue fun recipes to the pages, including the recipes you discover in this book.

At the beginning of class, I like to walk the garden with everyone. If lavender is the topic of that day, we visit the lavender plants and each student is given a wand to sniff and press between the pages of his or her journal. After we work in the garden, we talk about the folklore, history, cultivation and uses for the herb. Herbs are like people. Each herb has a life story. Sometimes the stories I tell include happenings in my life, or my students' lives. After the story, it is time for herb crafting. My students love to work with fresh or dried herbs to create something special they can take home. Mint bath sachets, rosemary garlands, lavender dream pillows, and herbal bookmarks are among the crafts they enjoy.

Club meetings always conclude with an herbal refreshment. We make a snack with the herb we studied that week. For example, if we learned about rosemary, we might taste rosemary gingerbread cookies. If we are studying lemon balm, we might drink a cup of lemon balm lemonade. Of all the recipes we have sampled, apple-thyme jelly is probably my students' favorite. We make it with fresh thyme from our garden. The jelly is delicious served on a cracker with cream cheese. At the end of each meeting, my students always want to know which herb we will be tasting next week.

Each chapter in this book features a special herb we grow in our garden. These seven herbs are lavender, lemon balm, rosemary, chamomile, mint, thyme, and rose. They are club favorites because they can be used in so many wonderful ways.

If you have these herbs growing in your yard, you are ready to begin. If not, no need to worry. It's quick and easy to plant your own herb garden. Your local nursery will most likely have herbs for sale at an affordable price, or you can order fresh or dried herbs online. Sometimes hardware or grocery stores have herbs for sale too. Both chamomile and lemon balm are easy to grow from seed. If you don't have a yard, all you need is a windowsill! Herbs will grow in little individual pots— just remember to put a dish under them to catch the water when you give them a drink.

As you finish reading the first chapter, find a comfortable place in your garden to sit and draw lavender. Be very quiet and slow your breathing. Study the shapes and lines of this magnificent herb. When you sketch the stems, leaves, and buds, you may really know and see lavender for the first time.

Don't worry if you're not great at sketching. Neither am I! In the beginning most of my students' drawings are simple, and many are disappointed in their effort. I teach them that the process is what matters most. When they take time to "be" with lavender, they grow a connection with this herb and with the garden community. It may well be the beginning of a treasured friendship with Mother Nature. Of course, as students continue to sketch a different herb each week, their skill improves. I see more detail, more life, in their drawings.

If you sketch the herb in your journal, write its name and a simple phrase describing your impression of it underneath the picture. You can write about anything that comes into your head, such as the spicy scent of the thyme or the soft furry texture of a lamb's ear. If you see a ladybug, hummingbird, or preying mantis that's as interested in the herb as you are, write about that too. Leave a blank page next to the drawing so you can add additional notes, clippings, or recipes at another time. If you have a camera, you can take photos, and add them to your journal, or share them with your friends.

The recipes included in the third section of each chapter are ideas for what you can do with the herbs you lovingly grow. When children (and adults) discover the many ways herbs can be used, they want to make them a part of their daily life. The recipes provide us with a purpose for planting and tending these generous green folks. Stuff a lavender sniffy in your pocket or sip a chamomile smoothie and you will most certainly be a fully-fledged member of our club.

At the end of the book, you will recieve a Junior Herbalist certificate, just like the one my students earn when they have graduated from the Herb Garden Club. Your connection to herbs doesn't have to end with the certificate. I hope this book gives you a life-long love for herbs and the ability to make tasty and useful things that bring you and others joy.

-Kathy

A Description of Crestwood Herb Garden

Our garden is a large rectangle that measures 16 feet by 42 feet. A 4 foot by 16 foot sidewalk made of square red pavers divides the garden into two planting areas. Eighteen round red pavers create a meandering pathway across the entire length of the garden. Smaller pathways lead to a tall rose tree, wind around the bay tree, and travel through the spearmint garden. The sidewalk and pathways invite children to visit every area of the garden without disturbing the soil and growing areas. Teachers often take their classes through the garden as they walk toward the library or computer lab.

Vegetables, shrubs, and seasonal flowers are planted alongside the herbs. In winter we often grow carrots, broccoli, cabbage, and kale. During the warmer months we make room for potatoes, onions, and garlic. There are two gardenia shrubs that bloom throughout the warmer months. An assortment of violas, daffodils, and snapdragons brighten our garden in the winter months. Marigolds, petunias, and rock rose all add color in the warmer months.

There are three garden landmarks that the students and I have grown to love over the years. The yellow rose tree, a bay tree, and a butterfly bush are easily recognized from across the schoolyard.

The yellow rose tree, once a small bush, was donated by a fourth grade student in the early years of the garden. I believe it is sixteen years old. Now ten feet tall, it produces at least 200 roses every spring. On a warm sunny day the sweet perfume from these roses reminds everyone to come and spend some time in the garden. Teachers often bring bouquets of these roses into their classrooms.

Our bay tree was just eight inches tall when it was planted twelve years ago. Now it is easily eight feet tall. The dark green leathery leaves have a sweet, nutmeg-like scent. Garden club students enjoy eating bay leaf rice pudding. To make the pudding, we gently simmer two leaves in a cup or two of milk.

Throughout ancient Greece and Rome, bay leaves were recognized as a symbol of wisdom and scholarly achievement. When garden club students are presented with a junior herbalist certificate at the close of their school year, they are also given a bay leaf bouquet or wreath. The leaves are a symbol of all they have learned and accomplished in the Herb Garden Club.

Finally, there is the butterfly bush. Clusters of lavender, honey-scented flowers bloom in spring and summer. Of course, we love the honey fragrance produced by these wand-shaped flowers, but we also want the butterflies to come and stay awhile. They help the bees pollinate our herbs. In the warm weather, they do. We love to watch them flitting about our garden In addition to the butterfly bush, butterflies like to sip the nectar from mint, thyme, marjoram, rosemary, and lavender.

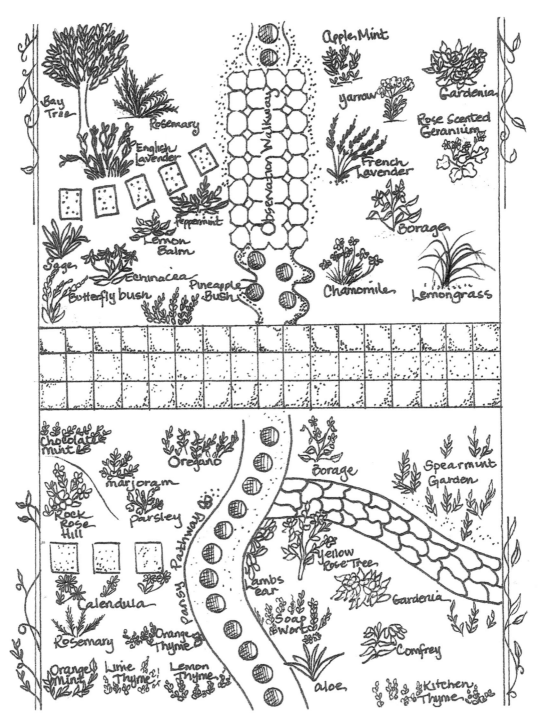

Map of Crestwood Garden by Sarah Garcia

What is an Herb?

An herb is a plant that can be used for medicine, cooking, crafts, or to take care of yourself.

The herbs you will read about in this book are easy to grow in a traditional garden. However, there are other herbs that can be found growing in the wild. Dandelions, horsetail and soapwort are examples of herbs that grow in meadows or along streams.

How many herbs do you know? Check the boxes and count your points (1 herb = 1 point).

☐ Lavender   ☐ Lemon Balm   ☐ Rosemary

☐ Chamomile   ☐ Thyme   ☐ Mint   ☐ Rose

Did you know some or all of the herbs above? Congratulations! You're well on your way to becoming a junior herbalist.

If you aren't familiar with any of the herbs in this book, welcome to the wonderful world of herbs! There are so many fun things you can do with herbs. They smell wonderful, can flavor hot or cold drinks or delicious food, and are handy as medicine too.

Herbs are as alive as you or I, and they have feelings. Scientists have shown us that herbs react when humans talk or sing to them.

If we take good care of herbs, they can give us a lot back. So next time you're feeling down, fill your room with the scent of lavender or drink a cup of chamomile tea with honey. Herbs have been used since ancient times to lift the spirit, brighten long days, and provide sustenance and medicine for humans. These special plants are easy to grow.

Let's get started.

Lavender

lavandula augustifolia

Meet Lavender

I am English lavender. My Latin name is lavandula augustifolia. I grow two to three feet tall. My narrow leaves range in color from pale green to blue or gray-green. Tall stems with fragrant purple buds and flowers appear in early summer. The best time to collect some of my flowered stems is in June or July.

There are over thirty different species of lavender. We all belong to the mint family because our stems are square. Visit a nursery or garden to get acquainted with us. Take time to smell our leaves and flowers. Without a doubt you will notice that my flower buds smell different than those of other lavenders.

Did you know that English lavenders are the hardiest? We can survive harsh cold weather throughout the winter. French and Spanish lavender need mild winter temperatures. Keep this in mind when you choose one of us to plant in your garden.

I like to be planted in full sunlight and well-drained, sandy soil. Harvest me in the early morning after the dew is gone. My flower buds can be used fresh or dried. To dry me, gather the flower in bunches. Secure each bunch with a rubber band. Hang the bunch, flowers facing down, in a warm, dry room.

Legendary Lavender

Lavender has a fresh clean fragrance that brightens the day. Its name comes from the Latin verb lavare, meaning "to wash." The ancient Romans and the Greeks were big fans of lavender, and scented their soaps and bathwater with this herb. Throughout medieval Europe, stalks of lavender were placed in linen closets to perfume sheets and blankets. Lavender was used as a strewing herb on the floor of houses and churches. As folks walked about, the pleasing aroma brought happy smiles to their faces.

Today lavender continues to scent the home. Lavender scented soaps and candles are available in gift shops and department stores. Sachets, tucked inside drawers and cupboards, sweeten underclothing and bedding. Small muslin bags filled with lavender are used as dream pillows. Place them under a pillow inside a pillowcase for a good night's rest.

Delicious things to do with lavender in the kitchen:

1. Add a bittersweet taste to ice cream, chocolate, honey, butter, and vinegar with lavender buds.

2. Use lavender flavored sugar to prepare cakes, sugar cookies, muffins, and lemonade.

3. Have you ever picked a garden ripe strawberry and dipped it in lavender sugar? Oh my, what a treat!

Here's to your health!

Brew a cup of lavender tea to relieve headaches.

Bathe in lavender infused water to feel relaxed and peaceful.

Apply lavender essential oil (distilled) directly to the skin to disinfect and heal scrapes.

War Wounds and Tea Cups

Many people use lavender as a medicine.
Long ago, Roman soldiers took lavender with them to dress their war wounds. During the 16th century, Queen Elizabeth I of England drank countless cups of lavender tea to treat her migraine headaches. By the 17th century lavender and lavender essential oil were used to calm nerves and treat insect bites. In modern times we continue to use lavender as a medicine.

Did you know?

In Roman times, one pound of lavender would buy 50 haircuts!

A Lavender Story

The college campus was almost empty over summer break, but twelve-year-old Lindsay was in a hurry. She passed a few fellow computer campers as she ran past the library. Class had just finished for the morning. She and eight other campers had been working on designing characters for a game. She had woken up late again, and had thrown on her black camp-issue t-shirt with the white logo. Lindsay had skipped breakfast, but she wasn't hungry. She felt heavy, as though her heart was weighing her body down.

She collected her mail and went up to her dorm room, launching herself onto the small single bed to read her mother's letter. A week had gone by since computer camp had begun, and somehow her excitement had died. She'd always loved working with computers, but it was strange, being away from her mother for the first time. She missed the fragrance of her mother's herbs, and her mother's arms as she hugged her before bed. The scent of lavender and rosemary did not seem to belong in the pale hallways of the dorm. Lindsay sat up straight on her bed. She was twelve

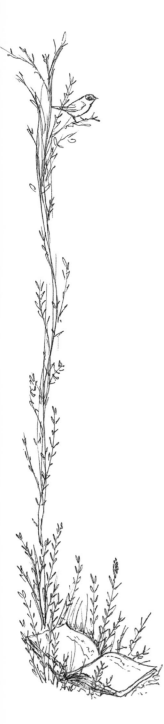

now. She had to be strong, not homesick. A robin was singing outside the window, as if to remind her that there were also gardens on campus, not just at home.

The envelope felt strange in her hands. Dozens of tiny little somethings slid from side-to-side as if they were playing a game. She coaxed the envelope open with her delicate fingers, tipping it sideways to peer inside, and laughed when a handful of soft lavender buds showered her kneecaps. She imagined she was walking along the pathway through her mother's gardens. If she were back home, she would pass by the thyme plants sunning themselves. Kitchen thyme shared the space with lemon, lime, and silver thyme. She would continue down the path, and pause by the tea garden. Lemon balm, peppermint, chamomile and rosemary were among the herbs that her mother used to make healing herbal teas for the family. Peppermint tea was her favorite because it was refreshing and always seemed to take care of an upset stomach.

In her mind, she reached the place where the lavender was planted. A variety of English and French lavender bushes clustered around a stately old maple tree. Lindsay imagined herself standing next to one of these bushes with a pair of garden scissors.

Softly she would say, "Lavender, may I cut twelve of your stems? You smell so sweet. I want to bring some of you into the house."

Though the lavender bush would not answer with words, she always silently gave permission. Lindsay smiled as she remembered cutting the stems and thanking the bush for sharing. Inside the kitchen, she had placed the lavender wands in her favorite crystal

vase and displayed it on the kitchen table for her family to enjoy while she was away at computer camp.

Lindsay read her mother's letter. She wished she could fill a vase with freshly cut lavender, so the dorm room would smell like home.

Then she remembered that there was a way to smell the sweet scent of lavender after all. That's what the buds were for! She poured the lavender buds into a small bowl filled with water. Then she placed the bowl by the dorm window. As the hot July sun warmed the water, fragrant oil from the lavender buds was released and lavender perfume filled the room. Lindsay felt peaceful and happy for the first time in days. The singing robin landed on her window ledge. He seemed curious about the lavender bowl. "I think I'll call you William," Lindsay said. "You can visit me whenever you get lonely." The robin chirped, as if he understood, then puffed out his little red chest proudly.

As she stood at the window, Lindsay saw her friend Kim heading toward the cafeteria. "Wait for me! I'll be right down," she called to Kim. Lavender and rosemary did belong in this new place, after all. They were in her heart, just like her mother and their herb garden back home.

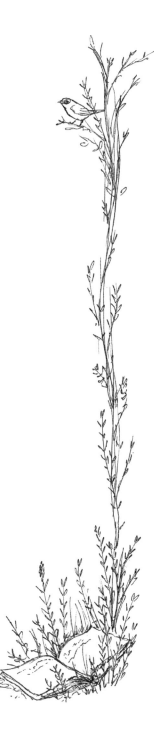

Lavender Sniffies

A sniffy is a mini sachet to hold, squeeze, and sniff. The uplifting scent will calm and relax you. Keep a l avender sniffy inside your pocket, in a backpack, or anywhere you can easily reach for it. Sniffies can also help you stay focused when reading or doing homework.

To make a sniffy, you will need:

Cotton fabric

Lavender buds

Small rubber band

Piece of yarn raffia or ribbon

Instructions:

1. Cut a piece of cotton fabric into an eight-inch circle.

2. Fill the center with a handful of lavender buds.

3. Lift the edges to form a bundle.

4. Secure with a small rubber band followed by a piece of yarn, raffia, or ribbon.

Lavender Christmas Sniffies

One year I decided to put sniffy ornaments on my Christmas tree. To give them a holiday scent, I blended dried roses, cinnamon stick pieces, and a few cloves with the lavender buds.

My granddaughters cut the circles from brightly colored seasonal fabric. They are now a yearly tradition. When stored in a glass jar or plastic bag, they will retain their marvelous scent year after year.

Lavender Doggy Powder

Dogs love the scent of lavender, and it's the perfect way to dry shampoo them, if you add baking powder. At one time I lived in the country with two Labrador Retrievers: one black, the other golden. Once a week I would brush them both with lavender powder. How they loved the fragrance! Labradors are happy animals. They easily smile and wag their tails. But when I brushed them with lavender, their blissful expressions were of the highest order and they kept me brushing.

I have read that lavender powder deters fleas when brushed into a dog's fur. Perhaps this is true because the Labs did not have a problem with fleas. I also sprinkled the powder on the cushions where they slept. In addition to deterring fleas, it may have helped them sleep well.

As with the lavender cookies, lavender powder is made with lavender buds and a spice grinder.

I sometimes add a few teaspoons of baking soda to the lavender powder.

When the baking soda is added, the lavender powder also absorbs odors and becomes a dry shampoo.

Important Note: **This powder is not for cats. Apparently the scent is too strong for them.**

Lavender Cookies or Cake

Years ago I began making lavender cookies for my fourth grade class. We all loved them and many students asked for the recipe. Then came the discovery of lavender cake. It was easy to make and somehow my students, family, and friends loved it even more. The pungent taste of lavender blended with moist, velvet white cake always left us wanting more. I know the lavender-tinted cream cheese frosting added to our delight.

Both lavender cookies and lavender cake are easy to make.

To make the powder:

Put a handful of dried buds into a spice grinder.

(A coffee grinder also works well if it is only used for herbs.)

Here's how you do it:

Add one or two teaspoons of finely ground lavender buds to your favorite butter cookie recipe.

One tablespoon of finely ground lavender can be added to any white cake mix or recipe.

Cream cheese frosting is a wonderful compliment for both the cake and cookies. As with the sprinkling sugar, the frosting can be tinted using a light lavender color using food coloring.

I have served this cake for Easter, birthdays, and most any special occasion. Lavender cake is delicious when served with vanilla ice cream.

Lavender Sprinkling Sugar

Oh what a great flavor this sugar gives lemonade and hot or iced tea! Lavender sugar can also be sprinkled on fruit salad or vanilla pudding. However, my favorite way to use lavender sugar is with fresh strawberries. Dip them in this sweet smelling sugar and you will fall in love.

To make lavender sugar you will need:

1 tablespoon dried organic lavender buds

2 cups granulated sugar

Instructions:

1. In a spice grinder, pulse the lavender with 1 tablespoon of the sugar.

2. Pour the finely ground lavender plus sugar into a bowl and stir in the remaining sugar.

3. Using red and blue food coloring, the sugar can be tinted a soft lavender color.

4. Transfer to a jar and cover tightly. Store for three days before using.

Note: A coffee grinder used only for dried herbs works as well as a spice grinder.

Lavender Dream Pillows

Folks have been making dream pillows for centuries. Ancient stories tell of herbs that calm the restless sleeper and bring good dreams. Lavender is one of the most common herbs used in dream pillows.

To make a dream pillow, you will need:

Soft fabric

Dried lavender buds

Fabric glue

Instructions:

1. Cut a 6-by-12-inch piece of soft fabric and fold it in half.

2. Squeeze a narrow strip of fabric glue along the two edges and allow the seams to dry.

3. Loosely fill the pillow with dried lavender buds.

4. Close the bag with another strip of fabric glue.

5. Slip this small lavender pillow inside your pillowcase and enjoy lavender scented dreams!

6. (optional) Add a few dried rose petals or a bit of chamomile to the lavender inside your dream pillow. This may make your dreams even sweeter.

The calming scent will be released each time you squeeze it or move your head while sleeping. My pillow case always has a dream pillow inside.

Lavender-Scented Rooms

I love to scent my home with lavender. Try it, and see how you feel. The uplifting, comforting fragrance of this herb brings new meaning to the words, "Home Sweet Home." If it's hard to concentrate on homework after a busy day, or if you're feeling blue because of events at home, school or work, lavender is a great way to clear your cluttered mind and restore your spirits.

To Scent a Room with Lavender:

Place a bowl of lavender buds and water by a sunny window on a hot summer day.

Keep a pot of lavender buds and water warming in a small crock-pot.

Place bowls of lavender buds near doorways to repel mosquitoes.

Put a vase filled with wands of freshly cut lavender in your room.

Tuck lavender sniffies in drawers, cupboards, and linen closets.

Lemon Balm
melissa oficinalis

Meet Lemon Balm

I am lemon balm. My Latin name is Melissa officinalis. Like lavender, I am a member of the mint family. My crinkly, lemon-scented leaves fill everyone with cheer after just one sniff. So don't be shy. Put your hands on me as often as possible. Nicholas Culpepper, a British herbalist of the 17th century, once wrote, lemon balm . . . "causeth the mind and heart to become merry."

You can purchase me from a local nursery, but I'm easy to grow from seed. Plant me in moist, well-drained soil and full sunlight. My tiny white flowers appear in the summer months. During the first year, I may seem scrawny with few leaves. In the second year, I usually grow two to three feet tall and produce a fine harvest. If you want to grow me indoors, I will need four or more hours of sunlight every day.

My leaves can be dried by hanging them upside down in small bunches. They can be laid individually on a screen or in a basket. Dried, my leaves are fragile, almost like tissue paper. They can be used to make tea.

I have a pleasing lemon fragrance so of course lemon became a part of my name. The word balm means "that which soothes."

The oil in lemon balm leaves will help you feel calm and relaxed. This is one reason why people enjoy sipping a cup of lemon balm tea, hot or cold.

Another name for me is "melissa." Melissa is the Greek word for honey bee. Both bees and butterflies love to visit me. Beekeepers often planted me around their hives. It has been said that bees like lemon balm more than any other herb. They use it to get their bearing and find the hive again.

Lemon balm, like many other herbs, was used by early civilizations. The Greeks used my leaves as a poultice to lessen the pain in skin wounds. Roman soldiers also used lemon balm as a healing poultice. They believed the leaves stopped the bleeding and the infection. Arab tribes drank my tea to relax and get a good night's sleep.

Lemony-licious!

If you don't love lemon balm in your food, you haven't tried it yet.

Toss a handful of whole or chopped leaves into salads.

Flavor fruit punch, fruit juices, or iced tea with these lemony tasting leaves.

Enjoy lemon balm in cooked vegetables like corn, broccoli, or green beans.

(Be sure to add the leaves just as the vegetables are finished cooking. Heat destroys the oils in lemon balm's leaves)

Banish Bad Bacteria

Sip lemon balm tea throughout the day when you have a cold or the flu.

Drink lemon balm tea to soothe your stomach after a large meal.

Clean cuts and scrapes with cooled lemon balm tea (The oil of lemon balm seems to inhibit bacteria).

A Lemon Balm Story

Yellow was Tomas's favorite color, because yellow was the color of lemons. Tomas loved the fresh citrus scent and sweet, sour taste of lemons, especially in lemonade. In second grade he planted his own tree in the backyard. Three years later the tree was taller than Tomas and produced dozens of bright yellow lemons. William the robin often perched on the lemon tree's slim branches. Tomas picked the lemons to make tall pitchers of lemonade. He wanted to drink all of the lemonade himself, but saved some to share with his family and friends.

One day, Tomas's mother brought home a small plant named lemon balm. She said, "Tomas, I bought this plant for you. Pick one of its leaves, rub it between the palms of your hands, and enjoy the scent."

Tomas rubbed the delicate leaf between the palms of his hands. To his surprise, a luscious lemon fragrance wafted from the leaf. It delighted him. He had no idea there was another way to savor the fragrance of lemon.

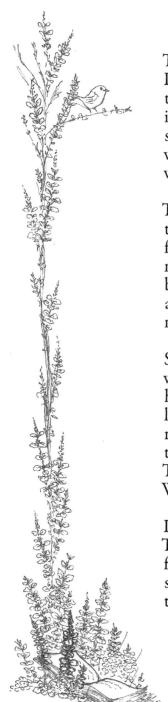

Tomas placed the lemon balm plant on a table in his bedroom. Looking at the bright yellow green leaves filled Tomas with sunny thoughts. However, one day the lemon balm plant stopped smiling. Its leaves drooped and Tomas discovered his plant needed more sunlight. He decided to plant it outside, just below his bedroom window. William would visit the plant every morning and Tomas would wake up to his song.

The lemon balm plant loved being outside under the sun. She grew taller and leafier while listening to William's cheerful song. The following year she grew to be two feet tall. Her seedlings sprouted nearby. Tomas loved to open the window so he could smell lemon balm's sweet perfume. Sometimes he picked a few leaves to float in a bowl of water. Watching the leaves mingle with water, Tomas remembered the delicious sun tea his mother sometimes made.

Since his mother was out shopping, Tomas decided to surprise her with a lemon treat when she returned home. He went outside to harvest a handful of leaves from his lemon balm plant. A few of the leaves were tossed in William's birdbath. Tomas lightly rinsed the remaining leaves at the kitchen sink and placed them inside a sun tea jar. He filled the jar with cold water and fastened the lid. Then Tomas carried the jar outside, placing it in full sunlight. He noticed William happily splashing about in the birdbath.

Later that afternoon Tomas brought his lemon balm sun tea inside. The jar was warm and the liquid was a light, golden color. Tomas filled a glass with ice. He poured the tea into the glass and took a sip. How refreshing! The iced herbal tea had a soft lemon flavor that tasted so good on a hot summer day.

While Tomas drank the lemon balm tea on the backyard deck, he admired his lemon tree. There were at least seven bright yellow lemons ready to be picked. Tomas gathered four of them to make lemonade. He thought to himself, why not add the lemon juice to the lemon balm tea? Tomas poured the tea and the lemon juice into a pitcher. One sip of this strong lemon brew reminded him that honey was needed. Adding the honey a little at a time, Tomas created a recipe to share with his family and friends.

When his mother came home, Tomas served them both a glass of his refreshing lemon beverage. They sipped the lemon balm lemonade as they talked about their day. Feeling relaxed and happy, Tomas poured them both another glass. The lemon tree smiled, pleased that he was able to share his fruit with them.

Lemon Balm   51

Lemon Balm Lemonade

Lemon balm lemonade is delicious! You can try making it at home. All you need is:

2 cups lemon balm tea

1/2 cup honey

1/2 cup lemon juice

Lemon slices for garnish

A Birthday Fiesta Lemonade Story

Tomas received an email invitation to cousin Javier's birthday party. He finished his glass of lemonade and poured himself another, while he read the invitation. As Tomas enjoyed his recipe, a sunny smile played across his face. Lemonade was always a treat. When he drank lemonade made with lemon balm tea, Tomas felt peaceful and happy. He had the sense that all was right with the world. Thinking about the good feeling he had after drinking lemon balm lemonade, Tomas decided to name it "Tomas's Feel-Good Lemonade." He wanted to bring something special to the party, so he thought, why not bring something homemade?

The following week, Tomas and his family attended cousin Javier's birthday fiesta. Grandparents, aunts, uncles, and lots of cousins came together to celebrate the special day. Mama brought her green chili enchiladas. Tomas made two gallons of his Feel-Good Lemonade for everyone to sample. He wondered if they would like it.

There was music, laughter, and lots of delicious food. There was also an unusually tasty lemonade that everyone loved.

"Tomas, promise me you'll bring your lemonade to our next fiesta," cousin Javier said.

"Sure thing," Tomas answered. "It's a promise!"

As the years went by, Tomas always brought his Feel-Good Lemonade to family gatherings. It became a tradition that everyone enjoyed.

Sometimes an aunt or uncle would ask for the recipe. When Tomas shared his recipe, he also brought a small pot containing one of the young lemon balm plants from his backyard. His family would need to grow their own lemon balm if they wished to make the lemon beverage regularly. He wished all his relatives and friends would grow lemon balm and make the special lemonade. As Tomas often said, this world would be a happier place if everyone drank lemon balm lemonade. William the robin couldn't have agreed more.

Lemon Balm Ice Cubes

Lemon balm ice cubes are festive and fun to use on a hot summer day. Float them in a glass of water, iced tea, fruit juice, or punch. I love to watch the bright green bits of lemon balm and fruit circling a warm weather beverage. As the cubes melt, those little pieces of lemon balm and fruit are a special treat.

To make lemon balm ice cubes, you will need:

5 or 6 fresh young lemon balm leaves

Sliced strawberries, oranges, or lemons

Water

Ice cube trays

To make the recipe:

1. Harvest five or six fresh young leaves from a lemon balm plant. Wash and tear them into small pieces.

2. Distribute the pieces evenly on the bottom of an ice cube tray.

3. Add a small piece of sliced strawberry, orange, or lemon to each cup.

4. Fill each cup in the tray halfway with water. Then place the tray in the freezer.

5. When the cubes are frozen, add more water and return to the freezer. This two-step process assures that the leaves and fruit will be frozen deep inside the cube.

6. If you want to make clear ice cubes, boil and cool the water before filling the tray.

Green Salad with Lemon Balm

Though many children are not fond of green salads, garden club students enjoy the pairing of lemon balm leaves and sliced red onion. They just taste good together.

To create this tasty salad, you will need:

Lemon balm leaves

Red onion, sliced

Lettuce

Light vinaigrette dressing of your choice

Always keep the ingredients in this salad simple.

Instructions:

1. Gather a handful of fresh young leaves from a lemon balm plant. Wash and dry them.

2. Then add the leaves and rings of sliced red onion to a lettuce salad.

I use a few basic types of lettuce along with the lemon balm and onion. In doing so, the delicious flavor of lemon balm and red onion are allowed to be the stars of this show.

After the salad has been prepared, I toss the leaves and sliced onion. I then set aside the salad for ten to fifteen minutes so that the lemon balm leaves can infuse the rest of the salad with their garden-fresh citrus flavor.

Just before serving, sparingly add a light vinaigrette to the salad.

So simple and yet so delicious! Try it for yourself. It's an easy way to help out with dinner, or to make a healthy after-school snack for you and your friends.

Lemon Balm Longevity Tea

Lemon balm is a perfect tea herb. Sipping a cup of this refreshing tea lifts the spirits and brings sunshine into your day. Taken after a large meal, it relaxes your stomach and relieves indigestion.

To prepare this tea, you will need:

Lemon balm leaves

Water

To sweeten: add honey, sugar, or stevia

Optional: mint or strawberry leaves

Instructions:

1. Place a small handful of young leaves in a pot of freshly boiled water.

2. If you wish, add a few mint or strawberry leaves.

3. Steep for eight to ten minutes. The tea can be served hot or cold over ice. To sweeten, use honey, sugar, or stevia.

If you wish to drink a cup of lemon balm tea everyday, you may live a long and healthy life.

John Hussey, a gentleman who lived in Sydenham, England, drank lemon balm tea with honey every day for fifty years. He lived to be one hundred and sixteen.

Llewelyn, Prince of Glamorgan, also drank lemon balm tea daily and lived to be one hundred and eight.

Scented Book Pages

Have you ever opened a book and enjoyed reading herb scented pages? No? Then you're missing out! Throughout history, mint and rose petals have been slipped between the pages of books. Lemon balm is one of my favorite herbs to use for this purpose.

To Scent a Book with Lemon Balm:

Pick fresh leaves midmorning after the dew has dried. Place them between the pages of your favorite book. Then close the book and let the leaves infuse their soft lemon fragrance into the pages. Next time you open your book, you'll enjoy the uplifting, cheerful fragrance as you read.

If you want to be adventurous, gather a collection of three of four herb leaves or petals along with lemon balm. Let your nose do some thinking. Which leaves or petals have scents that go well together?

I like to blend lemon balm leaves with rose petals, mint, and small sprigs of thyme.

Be sure the book you use is your own! Library books or a book borrowed from a friend are not appropriate for this activity.

Shoe Freshening

Every morning we put on a pair of shoes. They protect our feet and go everywhere we go. Sometimes they walk miles. At the end of a long day, we give them a chance to rest. More than likely they carry a little foot odor.

To freshen shoes and prepare them for another active day, at night tuck a lemon balm sachet inside each one. Shoe sachets are effective and easy to make.

To make a sachet, you will need:

Lemon balm leaves

Rubber band

Piece of ribbon or raffia

Cheesecloth (this is available to buy at grocery stores or any store that sells kitchenware, and was traditionally used to make cheese)

Then:

1. Wrap a handful of freshly harvested lemon balm leaves inside an 8-inch circle of cheesecloth.

2. Lift the edges to form a small bag and close with a rubber band. Tie a piece of ribbon or raffia around the rubber band for a decorative effect.

3. The following morning you will

enjoy putting on your garden-fresh lemon-scented shoes.

The closet will smell good, too. Mint or other herbs can be also be added to your shoe sachet. Have fun experimenting with sachet recipes.

A Lemon Balm Lavender Bath Bag

While lemon balm is a perfect herb for your teapot, it is also a wonderful herb to use in your bathtub. When used as bathing herbs, both lemon balm and lavender combine to clear away the stresses of the day from your mind and body

Ingredients for a lemon balm lavender bath:

4 Lemon balm leaves

Lavender buds

Rubber Band

Muslin piece, about 8 inches in diameter

To make your lemon balm lavender bath:

1. Gather fresh lemon balm and lavender buds and flowers from your garden.

2. Cut a piece of muslin into an 8-inch circle.

3. Fill the center of the fabric with a handful of lemon balm leaves and lavender buds.

4. Lift the edges to form a bundle and close with a small rubber band.

5. Drop the bag into the bath water and give at it least five good squeezes. The oils from the leaves and buds will infuse the water.

6. For a soothing, relaxing soak, climb in and stretch out. Breathe in the wonderful garden

Lemon Herb Garden

Planting a lemon herb garden is easy, and really fun to do. There are several herbs that have a lemon scent. You've probably heard of some of them. Lemon verbena is popular in ice cream, and lemon basil paired with chicken is a favorite on restaurant menus. Lemon cake bars can be made with lemon thyme instead of lemons.

Both lemon grass (an essential ingredient in many Thai dishes), and lemon mint are fun to grow. Don't forget to include lemon balm!

When I first became interested in herbs, it was a surprise to learn that so many herbs were lemon scented.

At once I began to grow them along a pathway in my backyard. Later the garden club students helped me plant them in the school garden. We wanted to get acquainted with the lemon herbs.

Each one of these herbs carries its own unique scent and flavor. Young lemon balm leaves have a soft citrus smell while lemon verbena are known for their sweet floral fragrance.

Clip a piece of lemon grass and enjoy a bright lemon scent followed by a hint of grass. The smell of lemon thyme reminds me of a lemon verbena leaf that has been paired with common thyme.

While lemon basil and lemon mint are not commonly available in my local nurseries, I have been able to order them online. The scent of lemon is divine when blended with basil or mint.

A delicious roundup of lemon herb treats:

I hope you enjoyed all the lemon herb variations and the recipe ideas! Lemon herbs are a favorite of people all over the world. They can be used in cooking, in medicine, or even soap making. I hope you will decide to grow a lemon scented herb garden so you can compare their scents and explore new ways to use them.

Rosemary

rosemarinus officinalis

Meet Rosemary

I am Rosemary. My Latin name is rosemarinus officinalis. The name rosemary means dew of the sea. Rosemary is a fitting name for me because I have a great love for sunshine and moist salty air. My sweet-smelling leaves have an aroma that reminds me of pine needles. I am often seen growing in clusters along California beaches.

There are many varieties of rosemary. Some of us have blue flowers. Others have pink, violet, or white flowers. We like to be planted in soil that drains easily. I am one of the varieties that grows upright but some types of rosemary are low growing and make a fine ground cover. Upright rosemary will reach three to six feet high. Low growing rosemary stands no taller than 20 inches.

My short needle-like leaves dry easily. Collect five or six of my stems or branches. Wrap a rubber band around them to form a bundle. Hang the bundle in a dark place that has good air circulation. Remove the dried leaves from the stems and store in a glass jar

Grow Your Own Friends

Rosemary is known as a symbol of remembrance, friendship, and love.

If you grow a rosemary bush in your yard, it is said you will never be short of friends. Brides once wore wreaths woven with sprigs of rosemary, or carried rosemary in their bouquets. During funerals, mourners tossed fresh rosemary stems into the grave. The stems were a sign that the life of the loved one would be remembered.

Ancient Brain Power!

Long ago Greek and Roman students placed stems of rosemary behind their ears to improve their memory. During a difficult test, they would wear a rosemary wreath on their heads. Today many people still believe that rosemary's scent improves our ability to think and remember. Students of all ages sniff sprigs of rosemary when they do homework or study for a test.

Spice Up Your Food
(and Your Campfire)

Is your chicken too bland? Rosemary's a fun herb to cook with. It has a pungent, peppery flavor that can spice up plain food without much effort. Whenever I eat woodsy-scented rosemary, it reminds me of camping out, and eating honey-rosemary chicken sandwiches under a pine tree in the woods.

Tasty Rosemary can be used to:

Season chicken, lamb, soups, and potatoes (add rosemary to split pea soup for a tasty winter treat)

Bake breads, cakes, and cookies

Flavor salads, rice, or cooked vegetables

Banish Bee Stings

Rosemary has been used as a healing herb for hundred of years. Throughout Europe it was used to soothe wounds and mouth sores. It was also made into a poultice for bee stings, bites, and aching muscles. Today people drink Rosemary tea to treat colds, flu, sore throats, and headaches. The tea has a strong, somewhat bitter taste, so you may wish to add a teaspoon of honey. Combine the healing powers of rosemary and green tea for a fun variation on rosemary tea.

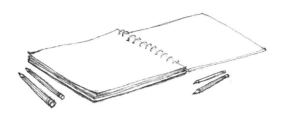

A Rosemary Story

On Sidney's birthday, the mail carrier delivered a birthday card from Grandma and Grandpa. William the robin was eating a worm for breakfast and saw the delivery. He peered in through the window to see why Sidney had mail. She hardly ever received letters. Sidney opened the card and found three crisp ten dollar bills inside. How wonderful! Maybe her mother would take her to the mall.

"Mom, Grandma and Grandpa sent me birthday money. Will you take me shopping this afternoon?"

"Sorry Sidney, I'm just too tired."

Sidney was disappointed. She wanted to buy a new sketchpad and some colored pencils. Almost every day Sidney drew something–the neighbor's cat, an old shoe, a butterfly, or the daisy bush outside her bedroom window.

Now that her first sketchpad was filled, Sidney wondered how she could draw without a pad. The lined notebook paper in her binder was not acceptable. A real artist must have a drawing pad. Sidney

walked into the kitchen. Her mother was putting away dishes. She still looked tired.

"Mom, I'll run some bathwater. You always feel better after a bath."

"Thanks, Sidney. That's a good idea. But please don't think I'm going to change my mind about going to the mall."

"I know, Mom. I just want to help."

The truth was, Sidney had a secret plan that she believed would change her mother's mind.

Before running the bathwater, Sidney walked outside with a pair of scissors. She cut two long stems from her mother's rosemary bush. Sidney knew that rosemary leaves are filled with energy. She cut each stem into three, four-inch pieces. Then she laid the three pieces on an eight-inch square, cut from an old t-shirt. Lifting each corner, Sidney formed a bundle and tied it closed with a string.

Sidney turned on the bathwater. She held the rosemary bundle under the stream of warm running water. After a few minutes, Sidney threw the rosemary bundle into the bath water. Pine-scented oils from the leaves continued to infuse the water.

Soon Sidney's mother was relaxing in the rosemary bath. Twenty minutes later her mom was dressed and smiling.

"Sidney, I feel great! The rosemary you put in the bath water worked wonders. Let's go shopping!"

Later that afternoon, a smiling Sidney drew a picture of rosemary in her new sketchbook. Her colored pencils came in many rich shades, including greens, grays, blues, and browns. Those were the colors Sidney used to draw her mother's rosemary bush. William perched on a nearby branch and watched. Robins couldn't draw, of course, but he admired humans that could.

The following day Sidney visited Mrs. Greenley, her next-door neighbor. Mrs. Greenley loved herbs and had a garden filled with them. In fact, it was her herb-loving neighbor who taught her how to prepare a rosemary bath.

"Guess what, Mrs. Greenley? Yesterday I put rosemary in my mother's bath water."

"How did she like bathing with rosemary?" Mrs. Greenley asked.

"I think she liked it a lot because she was happy and full of energy. Mom even took me shopping to buy colored pencils and a sketch pad. Mrs. Greenley, I want to show you a picture I drew. Can you guess what it is?"

"Why, that's rosemary!" Mrs. Greenley exclaimed. "It looks just like the bush growing in your backyard."

"That's it! That's exactly what I drew."

"You are a fine artist, young lady. In fact, you seem to have a talent for drawing the green world."

"Thanks Mrs. Greenley. I was thinking... maybe I'll draw portraits of the herbs that grow in your garden. Then I can make an art gallery with them on my bedroom wall."

Mrs. Greenley chuckled. "I had an herb art gallery on my wall when I was a child. You're welcome to visit the herbs anytime, as long as you give me a tour of your art gallery when it's finished."

Sidney walked home, excited about spending time in Mrs. Greenley's garden. She wanted to draw the herbs, but she also wanted to learn more about how to use them. Sidney considered rosemary a helpful friend. Maybe there were other herbs who would share their gifts with her. William fluffed his feathers as he watched Sidney stroll home. Robins had always known about the secrets of herbs. It was surprising more humans didn't know about them.

Rosemary Gingerbread Cookies

Rosemary is often used to flavor meat, poultry, and vegetables. It can also be used to prepare cakes, cookies, jelly, and even lemonade.

One of my favorite sweet recipes is rosemary gingerbread co kies. The ginger and molasses in this recipe seem to come alive when rosemary is added. I like to make these spicy cookies in fall and winter when the days grow shorter and cooler.

To make these cookies, you will need:

A box of gingerbread mix from the grocery store

Dry powdered rosemary

Then:

Simply follow the directions for making cookies and add one teaspoon of dry powdered rosemary.

Powdered rosemary can also be added to your favorite ginger or molasses cookies recipe. These cookies are the tastiest when they are still a bit soft to the touch.

Powdered rosemary is easy to prepare. Put dried rosemary needles in a spice grinder or coffee grinder. Grind the needles until they are completely powdered.

Rosemary Salt

Years ago I discovered rosemary salt while shopping at a farmer's market. I bought a small jar and began to sprinkle it on meat, potatoes, and vegetables. This bittersweet herb is a wonderful flavor enhancer. It adds pizazz to so many foods. I particularly enjoy rosemary salt on roasted chicken. My husband likes to use it when he barbecues steaks or lamb chops

To make your own rosemary salt, you will need:

1/2 cup freshly harvested rosemary

1 cup kosher or sea salt

A food processor or blender

Instructions:

1. Toss the fresh rosemary needles in a food processor.

2. Process the rosemary needles until they are chopped just enough to release their oil.

3. Add salt and process until the rosemary and salt are well combined. (The salt will be a greenish color with small pieces of rosemary throughout. Freshly prepared rosemary salt is moist because of the oil in rosemary's leaves.)

4. Spread on a cookie sheet to air dry, or bake in the oven for 10 minutes at 225 degrees Fahrenheit.

5. Store in an airtight mason jar.

One to one-and-a-half teaspoons of celery salt can be added to your rosemary salt. It adds a little more interest to the flavor.

Homework Helper

Ancient Greek and Roman students relied on rosemary to improve their memory. Today rosemary continues to be used by students who want to do well on assignments and tests. Students in my fourth grade class often took rosemary stems from the school garden to rub and smell when completing a test or doing homework. They claimed the strong pine scent helped them concentrate, especially when answering a hard question.

If you have a rosemary bush growing in your yard, harvest three or four stems when it is time to do homework.

Lay them on the table or desk where you work. Now and then rub the rosemary needles with your fingers and hold the stem close to your nose. Rosemary helps your mind stay active and alert. Your homework will soon be done!

Friendship Bouquet

In popular folklore, rosemary is a symbol of friendship and remembrance. It has been said you will have many friends if there is a rosemary bush growing in your yard.

To create a bouquet:

Cut six to seven stems from a rosemary bush. Tie them together with yarn, ribbon, or a piece of raffia. You may wish to include other herbs in the bouquet. Lavender, thyme, rose, and peppermint are herbs that blend well with rosemary. Give this bouquet to a friend and you will be remembered

The Language of Herbs

Lavender: luck

Rosemary: remembrance

Peppermint: warm feelings

Thyme: courage

Rose: love

A Rosemary Bath
or Footbath

The Egyptians, Greeks, and Romans used the bath to refresh and restore mind and body. They believed in the healing power of water to bring relief from stress, sore muscles, and almost any discomfort in the body.

Today we can continue to enjoy the healing benefits of water. By using herbs in our bath, we can even design the type of bath we want to take.

Herbs like lavender, chamomile, and lemon balm help soothe and prepare us to sleep peacefully. Rosemary is all about energy.

Take a rosemary tub bath or foot-bath whenever you need energy. For directions on how to prepare a bath, refer to the rosemary story.

To make a footbath, rosemary can be used alone or with mint. It certainly does refresh tired feet.

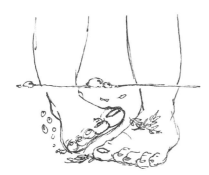

To Prepare the Footbath

1. Pour four quarts water and one cup of freshly cut rosemary (perhaps with a little mint) into a pot.

2. Bring the water and herbs to a boil.

3. Turn off the heat and let the rosemary infuse the heated water for one hour.

4. Reheat the rosemary water and pour into a foot basin.

5. Soak your feet for ten minutes or as long as you like.

6. When you are finished, pour the water and herbs into the garden.

A Winter Holiday Potpourri

Winter days can be bright and crisp, or dreary and gray. All too often the cold, gloomy weather can dampen our spirits. This is the time to pamper yourself with delicious foods, holiday music, and uplifting scents for the season.

To create a winter potpourri, gather the following herbs and spices:

4 bay leaves

4 rosemary sprigs, five to six inches long

6 cinnamon sticks

6 cloves

Rind of one orange

4 cups of water

Then:

1. Place the herbs and spices listed to the left in a pan.

2. Add the water and bring to a boil, then lower the heat and simmer on the stove.

Your house will smell wonderful as you wrap presents or bake cookies.

Chamomile
Matricaria recutita

Meet Chamomile

I am German chamomile. My Latin name is Matricaria recutita. The name chamomile comes from the Greek words kamai (on the ground) and melon (apple). When the two words are combined, they mean "apple on the ground."

There are two kinds of herbs known as chamomile. I am often confused with Roman chamomile. Roman chamomile is a low-growing plant, reaching no more than nine inches in height. In England, it is sometimes planted as a lawn. When walked upon, the apple scent is released. Roman chamomile is a perennial plant and will live for many years.

I have the same apple-scented daisy flower and feathery leaves as Roman chamomile. But unlike Roman chamomile, I stand two or three feet tall. My sprouts appear in the spring. In just a few weeks I grow to my full height. Warm spring days are my favorite. However, when hot summer days arrive, I disappear. If some of my flowers are left to drop their seeds into the garden, I will return year after year.

Both Roman and I are easy to grow. Plant us in full sun. Roman prefers a light, dry soil, but we will both grow in almost any soil that is well drained.

Harvest me in mid morning when my flowers are fully open. My little daisies can be laid on a screen or in a basket to dry. Once they dry, put them in a sealed jar. This will preserve the wonderful scent.

Chamomile Castles

In medieval England, people use chamomile as a strewing herb. Strewing or spreading chamomile on the floors of churches, castles, and homes was a common way to freshen the air.

Before refrigeration, folks placed meat in trays filled with chamomile tea. It was believed that the tea helped to do away with the rancid smell of aging meat.

For centuries women have used chamomile tea as a hair rinse. The tea is known to bring out the natural blond highlights.

Chamomile Daisy Decor!

Chamomile flowers are used to decorate cakes

Add the flowers to green or fruit salads

Float these little daisies in a party punch bowl

Add finely ground chamomile to smoothies

Chill out with Chamomile or Calming Chamomile!

Chamomile tea calms children and adults. It helps everyone sleep well.

Chamomile tea is used to relieve an upset stomach.

Do you have a sunburn? Add a bag of chamomile flowers to your bathwater. "Tea bathwater" will soothe and soften your skin.

Sickly plants feel better when given a drink of cooled chamomile tea.

A Chamomile Story

The moving truck was gone, and Mark Anderson's unfamiliar bedroom was a mess of stacked boxes. California sunlight warmed the walls of his bedroom but Mark felt lost. He opened his laptop only to discover there were no emails. His friends were too busy enjoying their summer vacation.

"Mark, are you ready? We're going to the bookstore!" His mother called up the stairs. He rolled off his bed, took a last look at the photo of his old friends in Michigan, and bounded down the stairs. His dad was waiting with the car keys in hand.

"Let's go check out the new store."

Mark forced a smile. His parents had been so excited about buying the bookstore in California. He'd said he didn't mind, but only because he knew how much they wanted to start a new life and do what they really loved. Mark had been fine with his old life. He was supposed to be starting fourth grade tomorrow. Now he'd be one of those kids that stood out, uncertain where to go. Friendless in the cafeteria. He sank deeper into the backseat of their car.

They drove downtown, his dad pointing out all the San Diego sights. "We could go to the zoo next weekend," he said.

Mark shrugged. "Sure."

"There's your new school." His mother beamed at him, but Mark felt his heart sink into his stomach. Nervous butterflies kicked in, as he looked up at the tall brick building surrounded by a parking lot and a baseball diamond.

"You'll make new friends in no time at all," his mother reassured him.

Mark said nothing. He had seen new kids try to fit in at his last school. It was hard to make friends when the other kids had already formed groups. And what if his teacher was mean?

The bookstore was sandwiched between a coffee shop and a printing press. It had a little patio with red umbrellas and iron tables, dusty and forlorn. His mother tutted. "We've got a lot of work to do before next week's opening."

"One step at a time," his dad said, smiling at Mark. Dad unlocked the door and they stepped inside. It was surprisingly neat and tidy. His parents had bought the store inventory as well. The shelves were stocked with books and journals on every subject.

Mysteries, science fiction, cookbooks, history, and photography were some of the choices. Mark wandered off to look at the children's section. There were colorful picture books, games, and even a few toys.

He flicked through a nature magazine while his parents walked around the store discussing how to prepare for the reopening event. By the time they were done, Mark had explored the whole store. It was much larger than he had imagined.

Later that evening Mark's stomach hurt. "I'm not feeling well," he told his mother. Without saying a word, his mom took her favorite blue teapot from the cupboard and made a pot of chamomile tea.

She poured a cup for Mark and one for herself. Then she stirred one teaspoon of sweet clover honey into each cup.

"Sip this and you'll feel better. The tea will help you fall asleep."

"Thanks," he said, sipping from his mug. It didn't taste as good as hot chocolate, but he liked it. He began to feel calm and peaceful. By the time he finished the tea, his stomach no longer hurt. He slept soundly that night.

His dad dropped him off at Jefferson School the next morning. A couple of kids said "Hi" to him as he headed to his homeroom. The teacher was nice, and didn't force him to introduce himself in front of the class like some teachers did.

"So you're Mark?" one of the students asked him, a freckle-faced boy with shocking red hair.

"Yeah," Mark said, liking the boy's friendly green eyes.

"I'm Michael. Want to play soccer with us at recess?" the boy asked, pointing to his friends. Mark did, and then sat with them at lunch as well. The kids in his class were welcoming and friendly, and before long, several months had passed.

The bookstore was doing quite well, thanks to his dad's ability to buy the right books. Using his graphic design skills, Mark's dad created beautiful ads and store flyers that brought customers their way. Mark helped design the store's website, and he was proud of it.

On the weekends, Mark often visited the store. Sometimes he helped people find the books, games and magazines they were looking for, and recommended books to kids his own age. He often helped his mom serve coffee or tea to the customers. When business was slow he would serve himself a cup of chamomile tea and relax on the patio.

The seasons passed, and one spring day his mother called him downstairs. "Let's start a garden!" she said. Mark planted dozens of brightly colored flowers in the front yard.

When every flower was in place, Mrs. Anderson brought a large glass pitcher filled with golden liquid. "Give each flower a drink of this garden nectar," she said.

"What's in the pitcher, Mom?"

"It's chamomile tea that I cooled to room temperature."

"Why would we water flowers with chamomile tea?" Mark asked in astonishment.

"When flowers are taken from their home in the nursery, to their new home in our front yard, they feel uncomfortable. Even taking them out of their container to plant them in this front yard is a big change for them. The chamomile tea calms and relaxes them. It helps them adjust to their new surroundings so they can use their energy to grow new leaves and flowers."

Mark laughed.

"What's so funny?" his mom asked, smiling.

"What you said reminds me of how I felt last September," Mark explained, while he watered the flowers. "I missed our old home and my friends in Michigan. I was nervous about going to a new school. You gave me a cup of chamomile tea and I felt much better. I never realized that plants could feel the way I do."

His mother hugged him, while Mark tried to wriggle away. She held onto him, laughing. "One hug won't kill you. I didn't know you felt that way about moving. You're happy now, aren't you?"

Mark nodded, and this time he let her hug him tightly.

"Chamomile is such a wonderful herb for people and plants," his mother said thoughtfully, when they had finished watering the plants. "Maybe we should plant some in the backyard."

They bought a packet of German chamomile seeds from a nearby home improvement store that afternoon. By reading the seed packet directions, Mark learned that chamomile needed a lot of sunshine. The seeds could be sowed into the soil in early spring or fall. Little sprouts would appear in eight to 14 days if the ground was kept moist.

Mark chose a sunny place in the backyard to plant the seeds. The next day he and his mother used hand shovels, called "trowels," to turn and loosen the soil. Then Mark visited the compost bin. He filled a bucket with dark, rich earth and brought it to the garden.

Mark and his mother blended the compost into the loosened soil. The composted soil was light and fluffy, a place where chamomile's roots could easily travel downward.

When Mark opened the seed packet, he was surprised to see how tiny chamomile's seeds were. He wanted to spread them evenly across the prepared soil, but they were so small.

"Add the seeds to a handful of gardening sand," his mother suggested.

When the seeds and sand were mixed together, Mark sprinkled them onto the soil. Because the sand was a different color than the soil, Mark was certain the seeds were where he wanted them to be.

Before leaving the garden, he watered the chamomile seeds with a soft mist. He used a spray nozzle that had a setting for newly planted seeds. Everyday Mark and his mother took turns keeping the soil moist. On the tenth day, many of the seeds had sprouted. By the end of the third week, the plants were about twelve inches tall. "They may grow as high as eighteen inches," his mother told him.

A couple of days later, Mark saw that dozens of pretty flowers had bloomed, with deep yellow centers that reached for the sun. He took some pictures of the flowers with his phone. Mark wished he could show his friends at school, but he didn't think any of them would appreciate chamomile the way that he did.

On a warm summer day, when the chamomile flowers were fully open, Mark's mother showed him how to gather them. With a pair of garden scissors, Mark cut some of the stems along with the flower. He had to be careful, because washing or even touching them could have damaged the delicate blossoms.

To dry the chamomile, Mark spread the little daises on baking trays lined with paper towels. Gently, he removed the stems from the flowers and discarded them. Mark placed the baking trays on a shelf in the kitchen pantry.

One week later, the little flowers were dry and ready to be stored. Mark carefully spooned them into a quart-sized canning jar. Before sealing the jar with an airtight lid, he took one last sniff of the deliciously fresh, apple fragrance.

It was amazing how the scent of those tiny flowers could provide such a wonderful feeling of peace and calm. Mark had no doubt that chamomile was one of Mother Nature's best accomplishments. He looked forward to his next cup of chamomile tea. Naturally it would be made with homegrown chamomile.

In the months that followed, Mark continually discovered new ways to use the chamomile he had grown in the garden.

Mark's Chamomile Garden Tea

Chamomile tea is gentle and soothing. If you have had a stressful day, be sure to drink a cup of this tasty tea. Sip this golden brew before bedtime, and you can look forward to a good night's sleep. Though chamomile tastes delicious as is, it can be sweetened with honey. If you wish, add a pinch of cinnamon to each cup.

To make a pot of Mark's chamomile tea, you will need:

2 tablespoons fresh or 1 tablespoon dried chamomile

2 1/2 cups boiling water

Then:

Put the chamomile in a pot.

Pour the boiling water into the pot. Cover with a lid.

Steep for 4 to 5 minutes. Strain and serve.

Chamomile Iced Tea with Apple Juice

The apple flavor of chamomile tea is delicious with apple juice. This tasty iced tea is calming and refreshing. Mark and Michael sometimes make this juice after they play soccer. A spicy sprig of thyme and sliced strawberries are the finishing touch. My garden club students give this recipe a thumbs-up.

To prepare this treat, you will need:

1 cup room temperature chamomile tea

4 tablespoons apple juice

1 sliced strawberry

1 sprig thyme

Ice cubes

Instructions:

Add the thyme and apple juice to the tea.

Pour over ice in a large glass.

Garnish with sliced strawberries.

Serves 1.

Chamomile Smoothie

If you love smoothies, and have a blender at home, try making this satisfying and easy summer drink. Chamomile tea enhances the flavor of peaches, blueberries, and bananas. Smoothie heaven is the place you'll go after drinking this nutritious beverage.

Ingredients:

1/2 cup chamomile tea

1 cup frozen blueberries

1/2 cup low-fat milk

1 teaspoon fresh ginger minced

1 peach skinned and chopped

1 tablespoon dried chamomile

1/2 banana

Directions:

Make an extra strong cup of chamomile tea.

Put the tea in the blender and add the remaining ingredients.

Blend well.

Serves 2.

Cooling Chamomile Spritzer

One day I was preparing a chamomile lesson for the garden club. I wanted to give students a complete chamomile experience. At our next meeting, students gathered to sketch the chamomile growing in the garden.

Returning to the library for a mini-lecture, there were bowls of dried chamomile to smell and touch. In addition, the room had been spritzed with chamomile tea. The students were smiling and appreciative. We all enjoyed our time with chamomile.

For a calming spritzer

Fill a small spray bottle with cooled chamomile tea.

Lightly mist this herbal water on your face, in your room, or on your pillow.

Refrigerate when not using

Closet Sachets

Have you ever walked into a chamomile scented closet? The sweet apple scent is warm and inviting. Reach for a t-shirt or sweater to wear and a wisp of this fragrance will welcome you.

Make several chamomile sachets for hanging in a closet or putting inside the drawer.

To make the sachets, you will need:

Dried chamomile flowers

Fabric

Small rubber bands

Ribbon

Directions:

1. Place a handful of dried chamomile flowers in an 8-inch square of fabric.

2. Gather the corners together.

3. Close with a small rubber band and decorate with a colorful piece of ribbon or raffia.

4. Loop it over a clothes hanger in your closet.

5. (optional) Rose petals or another herb of your choice can be blended with the chamomile flowers.

A Chamomile
Tea Garden

A chamomile tea garden is a fun and useful way to use herbs.

Tea herbs that blend well with chamomile:

Mint

Lemon balm

Thyme

Growing your tea garden

1. Tea herbs can be grown in a half-barrel, usually available at hardware stores.

2. Drill four holes in the bottom of the barrel and line the bottom with two inches of gravel.

3. Then fill it with some good soil that drains easily.

4. Next, add compost and mix it into the soil.

5. Now you're ready to plant the chamomile alongside the lemon balm, mint, and thyme.

Remember:

Keep the soil moist, watering more in the heat of summer.

Fun uses for herb teas:

Make hot or iced teas with the freshly picked leaves and flowers. In general, you will infuse 3 teaspoons of fresh, crushed herb in one cup of boiling water.

Lemon balm has a more delicate flavor and requires 4 teaspoons.

Chamomile and mint are a soothing tea to drink when you have a cold or the flu. Add honey to soothe a sore throat.

Thyme
thymus vulgaris

Meet Thyme

I am garden thyme. Some folks refer to me as common thyme. My Latin name is Thymus vulgaris. I am a shrubby plant, standing 9-12 inches tall. To find me in the garden, look for my tiny gray-green leaves and pale lilac blossoms.

There are as many as 130 varieties of thyme. Lemon and silver thyme, like me, are members of the thyme family that grow upright. There are also creeping thymes. These thymes form a low growing mat, reaching no more than four to five inches tall. Wooly, elfin, and golden thyme are members of this family.

We all grow best in light, dry, well-drained soil. Full sun is best for us but we will grow in partial shade.

Harvest me in midmorning, after the dew has evaporated. To dry my leaves, tie the stems together. Then hang them upside down in a shady, dry place.

When my leaves are dry, strip them from the stems and store in an airtight container. They will keep their strong flavor and aroma for six to seven months.

Courageous Thyme

Thyme has been popular since the days of ancient Greece. This busy herb will ramble up hills or down banks without anyone to tend or water it. Many scholars believe the word thyme is derived from the Greek thymus, which means courage. Scottish highlanders drank thyme tea to give themselves strength and strong-heartedness. Others believe thyme came from a Greek expression which means "to fumigate." This would make sense because dried thyme was burned to purify the air and chase insects from the house.

Many cultures throughout history have harvested this impressive herb. The Egyptians gathered thyme to embalm their dead. Greek and Roman men used thyme as a perfume. The Spanish, Italians, and French allowed their sheep and goats to graze in the fields of thyme. This fragrant herb gave the meat a wonderful flavor. In Columbus's day, sailors in foggy conditions could sometimes smell land before they saw it. Thyme and rosemary growing on the headland helped them smell their way home.

Tasty Thyme

Thyme has a delicate, green herby taste followed by a peppery aftertaste.

Toss leaves and flowers into a lettuce salad.

Flavor soups, casseroles, butters, and sauces with the tiny leaves.

Use as a seasoning for meat, poultry, and fish.

Healing Thyme

Treat sore throats, headaches, and coughs with a cup of thyme tea.

Use as a healing poultice. Apply fresh crushed leaves on small cuts and scrapes.

Greeks once used thyme tea to relieve asthma, whooping cough, and stomach cramps.

Thyme essential oil was used to disinfect soldiers' wounds in World War II.

A Thyme Story

Andrew could often be found in the back corner of the school library, delving into books about ancient history, and that was how he discovered that Roman soldiers used an herb called thyme. In those days, people believed that the lively spirit of thyme provided strength and courage. Roman soldiers often bathed in thyme or sipped thyme wine the night before going to battle. Sometimes they even slept on sprigs of thyme to prevent nightmares.

Andrew read that later, during the Middle Ages, the scent of thyme continued to inspire strength and courage. Knights carried thyme with them on their journeys. In addition, noble women embroidered a sprig of thyme onto the scarves of knights going off to battle. Sometimes the scarf would also contain the image of a bee hovering near a thyme flower. It was thought that the bee, who returns again and again to the flower, represents the warrior who will return home to his loved ones.

Andrew thought about the way thyme empowered medieval knights and ancient Roman soldiers, and wanted some thyme for himself. If only he could hold this plant in his hands and smell the scent of its leaves. Maybe then he would understand why thyme was valued by ancient warriors.

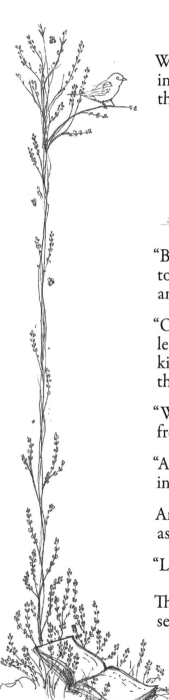

When he got home, Andrew found his father in the kitchen slicing an apple. "Dad, do you know anything about an herb called thyme?"

 "I sure do," his dad answered. He reached for a bottle of dried thyme from the spice rack. Dad removed the lid and invited Andrew to smell the sweet spicy leaves. Then he shook a few dried flakes into Andrew's hand. "That's thyme, he said. "Your mom and I sprinkle it into salad dressings, soups, and turkey stuffing."

"But Dad, this doesn't look anything like the thyme I saw in the history book. I want to know about the thyme that Roman soldiers and knights took with them when they went to war.

"Oh, you're talking about the fresh thyme that grows in gardens. The leaves from fresh thyme were dried to make the thyme we use in our kitchen. Our local nursery probably has some small pots of fresh thyme for sale," Dad said.

"Will you take me to the nursery?" Andrew asked. "I'd like to see the fresh thyme."

"Alright," his dad said, surprised. " I didn't think you were interested in gardening."

Andrew grinned. His dad loved gardening and looked really pleased as he fetched the car keys and put on his jacket.

"Let's go right now. Lunch can wait," Dad said cheerfully.

They drove to the nursery, and Andrew's dad led the way to the herb section, which he visited often. Andrew discovered a small pot of common thyme whose Latin name was written on the pot: *thymus vulgaris*. The leaves were tiny, but their pungent spicy scent was clean and refreshing. Andrew held the small herb under his nose, noticing how the smell was both relaxing and energizing.

"Dad, now I understand why the Roman soldiers and medieval knights liked thyme so much. Can we grow some in our garden?"

"Let's do it," his dad said enthusiastically.

That afternoon, Andrew and his father planted three thyme plants in the backyard. They found a sunny, dry location and spaced the herbs twelve inches apart. His father sprinkled one tablespoon of bone meal around the base of each plant.

"The bone meal provides nutrition to help the herbs grow," he told Andrew. "We need to give them another tablespoon each spring." Perched on a nearby maple tree, William watched as Andrew's father sprinkled the bone meal.

As the thymes began to flower in mid spring, Andrew noticed the bees visiting the newly opened flowers. William flew into the garden and sat next to Andrew. He sang one of his favorite songs, Ode to Spring, hoping the three thymes would know that winter was over.

Seeing the bees reminded Andrew of the scarves knights wore into battle. He wondered if the embroidered image of a bee hovering near a thyme flower might mean that people in the middle ages enjoyed thyme honey.

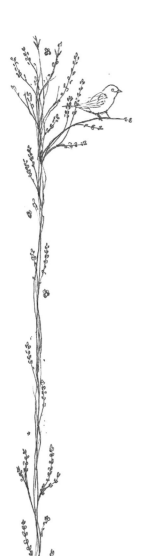

When Andrew read about thyme honey online, he learned that the honey had been popular for centuries. Virgil, the ancient Roman poet, was also a beekeeper. He praised the rich taste of honey drawn from the fields of thyme in both Greece and Sicily.

Of course, all that reading made Andrew want to taste thyme honey, but he found out it was not available in the local grocery store. So he found a recipe in an herb book.

Andrew's Thyme Honey

Gather:

1 empty glass jar

Enough fresh thyme to fill the jar

Honey (clover honey works well)

Andrew knew he could make the simple recipe himself but he invited his dad to join him.

Andrew's father loved to cook and he often prepared delicious meals with the vegetables and herbs growing in their garden. They found a large bottle of honey in the pantry and an empty 8-ounce jar in the cupboard. Andrew gathered the fresh thyme leaves and filled the empty jar to the top with sprigs of thyme from their garden.

His dad poured honey into the jar. As the honey rose, so did the thyme. Andrew used a chopstick to press the thyme down as the air bubbles rose. When all the air bubbles had popped, his dad filled the jar with a little more honey. Then he fastened the lid.

"Now we wait," his dad told him. "The honey will carry the strong flavor of thyme after six weeks."

Andrew and his dad looked at the jar of honey every day for a week, until they couldn't resist any longer. Andrew dipped a long spoon in the jar, and tasted the honey. Then his dad took a turn. "The honey is already infused with the taste of thyme!" his dad said, amazed.

"It's so good!" Andrew said, a spoonful of sticky honey in his mouth. They looked at each other and laughed, then scooped out more spoonfuls, savoring the delicious energy it gave both of them.

As the weeks went by, they continued to taste this marvelous sticky treat. Realizing that they were eating all the thyme honey, and soon there would be none left, they decided to make two more jars. One for Andrew and one for Dad.

Whenever Andrew read about how medieval knights and Roman soldiers used thyme as their ally, Andrew felt a connection to them.

He realized that the scent from just one sprig of thyme created a feeling of strength, and that gave him courage.

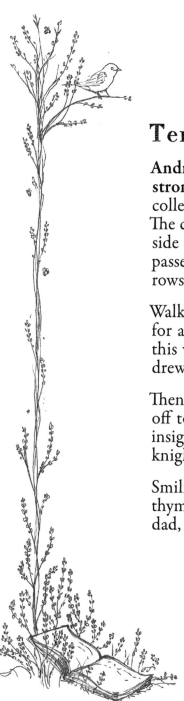

Ten years later

Andrew's interest in medieval knights and Roman soldiers grew stronger as he became older. A history major in his junior year of college, he was writing a paper about knights in the Middle Ages. The campus library was a six story limestone building on the south side of campus, its turrets reaching into the cloudless blue sky. He passed under the giant archway, and lost himself in the countless rows of books.

Walking among the tall shelves of history books, Andrew reached for a book that looked promising. Its worn, faded cover told him this volume was popular and had been borrowed many times. Andrew flipped through the pages.

Then he saw him. An English knight, seated on his horse, riding off to battle. Looking a little closer, Andrew noticed the knight's insignia, a honey bee and a flowering sprig of thyme, woven into the knight's scarf.

Smiling to himself, Andrew remembered the day he had first tasted thyme honey. One of his best memories was that of being with his dad, savoring one spoonful after another of thyme honey.

Herb Butter with Thyme

Herb butters are one of the most wonderful treats you can make with herbs. Butter absorbs the essential oils from herbs and preserves their fresh flavors. Herb butter can be served at the table to spread on bread. It is also delicious with baked potatoes or vegetables.

To make herb butter you will need:

8 ounces (2 sticks) butter, at room temperature

1/4 to 1/2 finely chopped thyme with a few other herbs (perhaps parsley, chives, basil, mint or oregano)

2 teaspoons lemon juice (optional)

Then:

1. Soften the butter.

2. Beat the butter in a medium mixing bowl with a wooden spoon or hand mixer.

3. Add the herbs and lemon juice. Mix until evenly blended.

4. Store in the refrigerator. It will keep for several weeks.

5. Freeze herb butter to use throughout the winter when the garden is sleeping

Green Chile Thyme Enchiladas

Green Chile Thyme Enchiladas are delicious any time of the year and everybody loves them. I make them for birthdays, holidays, and potlucks. My granddaughters often help me prepare them when they visit. Garden Club students love to eat them during our last meeting of the year.

You will need:

4 to 5 cups cooked shredded chicken

1 to 2 cups Mexican Blend shredded cheese

1/4 cup green onion or chives

Fresh thyme leaves to taste (about 2 to 3 tablespoons)

1 28- ounce can of Las Palmas Green Chile Sauce

12 to 14 corn tortillas

Coconut, olive, or vegetable oil

To cook the enchiladas:

1. Lightly cook the tortillas in coconut, olive, or vegetable oil.

2. Pour half of the green chile sauce into a 9-by-13-inch glass Pyrex dish. Dip the tortillas (both sides) in the green chile sauce.

3. Fill each tortilla with a portion of the chicken and cheese mixture. Roll into an enchilada.

4. Pour the remaining chile sauce over the enchiladas and bake 30 minutes at 350 degrees.

Apple Thyme Jelly

This is a special jelly you cannot buy in a grocery store. Fresh thyme infused into a good quality apple juice is the basis for this mouthwatering treat. It is a delicious spread for toast, crackers, or muffins. Oh so tasty with cream cheese!

You will need:

2 1/2 cups apple juice

1 cup fresh thyme

4 cups sugar

1/4 cup lemon juice

3 ounces liquid pectin

Making jelly is easy!

1. Bring the apple juice to a boil.

2. Pour over the fresh thyme.

3. Cover and steep until the juice has cooled.

4. Strain, removing all thyme from the liquid.

5. In a non-aluminum saucepan, combine two cups of herbal infusion with the sugar and lemon juice. Bring the mixture to a boil.

6. As soon as the sugar has dissolved, stir in the pectin.

7. Return to a rolling boil for exactly one minute.

8. Remove the jelly from the heat and skim off any foam.

9. Pour the warm jelly into sterilized jars.

Thyme Herbal Bath Bags

Do you remember the rosemary bath Sidney made for her mother? Like rosemary, thyme is a stimulating herb. Bathing with thyme infuses us with a calm, focused energy to use any way we wish. Lemon thyme has a light floral fragrance that is soothing and refreshing.

Bath Bag 1

Combine three tablespoons of dried thyme with two cups of oats.

Sew or tie into a small bag made from an old t-shirt or sock.

Use this "herbal sponge" in the bath or shower.

The combination of oats and thyme cleanses and softens your skin. You will feel energized!

Bath Bag 2

Put a handful of fresh lemon thyme into a muslin bag or an old sock.

Toss the lemon thyme bag into your bath water and enjoy a refreshing soak.

A Bundle of Courage

Earlier in this chapter, we learned that knights carried thyme with them on the way to battle. They believed the lively scent of this herb gave them strength and courage. Though you may not be a knight riding off to battle, making your own bundle o thyme might be a wonderful idea. In today's world, there are many times when all of us would like to feel strong and brave.

To make a bundle:
Cut seven or eight stems of thyme from a plant in your garden.

Bundle the stems together with a small rubber band and a piece of yarn or raffia.

Place the bundle in a place where you can enjoy the pungent scent of this powerful herb.

Feel free to add rosemary, lavender, or other herbs to your bundle. Thyme blends well with many of the herbs in your garden. You might want to make a bundle for a friend or family member.

Mint
mentha spicata

Meet Mint

I am mint. My Latin name is Mentha. Cool and refreshing, I am an herb that belongs in your garden. Peppermint and spearmint are two of the most popular species in my family. Orange, lemon, apple, chocolate, and pineapple are other members of the mint family often found in backyards.

All mints have fragrant green leaves that grow opposite one another on square shaped stems. We like moist soil and partial shade but will grow in full sun. Water us well and often in hot weather. Our underground stems, called runners, travel rapidly through the garden. Peppermint's runners can grow to be two or even three feet long. Experienced gardeners wisely plant us in pots or wooden planters. They love us but understand we could easily take over the garden, leaving little room for other plants to grow.

To harvest me, choose a fine sunny morning. Wait until the dew has dried. Then cut the leafy stems four to six inches above the ground. It is important to harvest me in the morning. My leaves contain an essential oil that gives me the refreshing flavor and scent I am known for. The essential oil in my leaves is strongest in the morning.

To dry, gather my stems to form bundles and hang me in a cool, dry place. Strip the dried leaves and flowers from the stems. Store them away from sunlight in airtight containers.

Minty Mind Control

The name mint comes from the Latin word mente, which means thought. Long ago people wore garlands of mint to inspire clear thinking. They believed the clean, minty scent freshened their minds as well as the air around them.

From earliest times, mint has been used and enjoyed. In ancient Greece and Rome, mint was used to scent baths and bedding. The Romans wore wreaths of peppermint to feasts and celebrations. They even decorated hallways and tabletops with this fresh scented herb. In Jewish temples, mint was used to purify the air for worship. Japanese men carried peppermint in small silver boxes that hung from their belts. They believed the fresh clean scent gave them energy throughout the day.

Today we can enjoy the flavor of mint in chewing gum, candy canes, ice cream, and after dinner mints. Mint is also a popular flavoring for toothpaste and cough syrup.

A Pinch of Peppermint in Your Punchbowl

Add fresh spearmint or peppermint leaves to salads, punch, and fruit juices

Simmer spearmint with fresh peas or carrots

Prepare brownies, muffins, and sugar cookies with peppermint

Drink Tea as the Colonials Did

American colonists drank a cup of peppermint tea to calm headaches, stomachaches, and nausea.

Taken at the beginning of a cold or the flu, a strong cup of peppermint tea may help you feel better.

Drink peppermint tea after a meal to improve digestion.

A Mint Story

One Saturday morning, Laura joined her parents for a workday in the backyard. The cool, crisp air put a spring in her step as she raked autumn leaves into a large pile. William the robin watched as Laura dropped armfuls of dry, crackling leaves into a red wheel barrow. Wanting to help, he put a leaf in his beak and placed it alongside the other leaves in the barrow. Laura thanked William with a smile.

When the wheel barrow was full, Laura dumped all the leaves into the compost pile. Then she worked hard to remove the weeds and crabgrass growing along the edge of the patio. Dad reminded her to loosen the soil so she would be able to remove the entire weed, root and all.

"Let's plant some pansies and snapdragons along the back fence," Laura's mother said. "But first we'd better clear away some of the peppermint. In fact, I think we need to remove all of it. Otherwise the runners will grow back and crowd the pansies."

Laura looked at the purplish-green peppermint. It was twelve inches tall and the runners had crawled everywhere. There was no space left to plant flowers.

"Mom, no," Laura said. "Peppermint makes our yard smell delicious. I love nibbling the leaves on a hot summer day. Isn't there another place we can plant it?"

"Well," her mother said, considering Laura's request, "we have a large terracotta pot sitting in the garage. We could plant some of the peppermint in that pot."

"I'll set the pot on the patio," Dad volunteered.

Laura and her parents filled the cheerful terra cotta pot with dark, moist soil from the compost bin. Laura and her mom took three peppermint runners from the back fence and replanted them in the pot. Finally, Laura gave the newly planted peppermint a drink with her watering can.

Meanwhile, Dad pulled the remaining stems and runners that were growing along the back fence. He had made a pile of them on the lawn. Soon they would be tossed into the green bin. William was upset that the peppermint would be tossed away, so he was glad when Laura spoke up.

"Wait!" Laura called. "Dad, don't take away all of the peppermint. I'd like some of it."

Dad looked frustrated. He wanted to finish the yard work.

"What are you going to do with it?" he asked.

"It's a surprise, Dad." Laura quickly filled her mother's garden basket with handfuls of the scented stems and leaves. Once in the kitchen, she emptied the basket of peppermint into a colander.

Laura rinsed away all the dust and dirt. Next, she separated the leaves and stems, tossing only the leaves into a large glass pitcher. As Laura poured water into the pitcher, peppermint leaves swirled and glided through the water.

Watching them through the glass, she could see how water brought the minty leaves to life. Their purple-green color was deeper and richer. The tiny veins that traveled through the leaves were more visible. Laura had never paid attention to the natural beauty of peppermint leaves until she saw them come to life in the pitcher of water.

As Laura started to pour peppermint water into three glasses, her mother entered the kitchen.

"What's this?" her mother asked.

"Oh Mom, this was supposed to be a surprise. I made peppermint water to serve you and dad. We did a lot of work this morning and it's time for a break. Peppermint water will give us energy to finish the rest of the yard work."

"What a great idea!" Mom took a sip. The cool minty water was refreshing.

"Laura, this is delicious just as it is, but I could put some orange slices into the pitcher. What do you think?"

"Let's do it," Laura said. "I love oranges." Mom cut an orange and added the juicy slices to the mint water. Laura took a sip. "Peppermint and orange slices are wonderful together."

Laura's mother helped her take three glasses and the pitcher of orange peppermint water outside to share with dad. The tasty water was brighter and even more colorful.

William was perched on a tree branch near the kitchen window. He had watched Laura's mother cut the orange. William loved orange slices too! When no one was looking, he snuck into the kitchen and landed on the countertop. One slice of orange remained on the cutting board. William pecked at it and then chirped with delight. The juice was sweet and delicious.

Outside on the patio, Laura and her parents finished drinking the orange peppermint water. Feeling refreshed, they planted the flowers along the back fence and while they worked, all three agreed that peppermint would always have a home in their backyard.

Teapot Mint Tea

There are at least 25 species of mint that come in a variety of flavors. Curly mint, apple mint, chocolate mint, spearmint, and peppermint are popular and easy to grow. A zesty hot tea can be made from any of the mints. However, peppermint is the most widely used for brewing tea.

Many drink peppermint tea because they like the zingy uplifting taste. A cup or two of peppermint tea is a refreshing way to start your day. It can also be the pick-me-up you need in the late afternoon. The British believe peppermint tea cleanses and strengthens the entire body.

To make mint tea, you will need:

A generous handful of freshly picked, washed, and torn leaves

Boiling water

A teapot

Then:

1. Fill the pot with boiling water.

2. Steep for six to seven minutes.

3. Serve in a teacup with a fresh leaf floating atop.

4. Peppermint and spearmint leaves blend well together.

Sunshine Mint Tea

For hundreds of years, Native Americans have used the sun as heat source to make herbal tea. The sun's rays heat the water without boiling away the natural flavor of the mint. This is a perfect warm weather tea for sipping on your patio or anywhere.

To make this tea you will need:

A one-quart canning jar

1/2 cup washed and torn mint leaves

Filtered water

Sunshine

Then:

1. Drop the freshly harvested mint into a canning jar.

2. Add water and fasten the lid. Shake the jar a few times, then place it outdoors where it will receive full sunlight throughout the day.

3. Bring the jar indoors and remove the mint leaves from the tea. Serve over ice cubes.

Peppermint, spearmint, and chamomile blend well together.

Minty Cucumber Salad

Thinly sliced cucumbers and fresh mint make this a refreshing summer salad. Garden club students love gathering the mint and parsley from our garden to make this tasty recipe.

You will need:

2 English cucumbers

Rind of one lemon

1 teaspoon salt

2 1/2 teaspoons sugar

1/8 cup chopped parsley

2 tablespoon red wine vinegar

1/4 cup chopped mint

2 tablespoon olive oil

Directions:

1. Remove the skin from the cucumbers and cut them in half lengthwise.

2. Use a teaspoon to scrape out the seeds.

3. Then cut the cucumber halves into thin slices.

4. Toss the slices with salt in a colander. Drain in the sink for 30 minutes.

5. Spread cucumber slices on a clean dishtowel. Use the edges of the dishtowel to blot the cucumber dry.

6. In a medium bowl, combine the cucumbers, parsley, mint, lemon rind, sugar, vinegar, and olive oil.

7. Cover and refrigerate for at least 20 minutes.

8. Enjoy your salad!

Peppermint Brownies

Chocolate and peppermint belong together. There are many dessert recipes that combine these two flavors but peppermint brownies are my favorite.

You will need:

1 cup chopped fresh pep-
permint leaves

Brownies mix

Prepared white frosting
(optional)

Peppermint extract
(optional)

Directions:

1. Heat to a simmer the liquid portion of your brownie recipe. Remove from heat.

2. Stir in the peppermint leaves. Cover and steep for 10 minutes.

3. Then uncover, cool, and add the liquid plus mint to the rest of the mix.

4. For a mintier flavor, stir a few drops of peppermint extract into a white frosting mix and ice the brownies.

Refresh Mint

In the early days of our country, the colonists knew that mint "cleared the head." They placed a mint blend in a decorative jar and used it as a desk accessory. Whenever they felt the need to freshen their minds, they shook the jar, then opened it and enjoyed the lively scent.

This is a version of the recipe they used:

2 cups each of dried peppermint, spearmint, and lavender

1 cup each dried thyme and rosemary

2-ounce glass jars with lids

Insructions:

Toss all the herbs together.

Leave them to age in a closed container for 24 hours.

Spoon into jars.

At Crestwood Elementary there are students who use Refresh Mint to complete homework. The lively scent helps them think and concentrate. Seniors at a local retirement home also like to use Refresh Mint. They say the aroma helps them stay awake when they are reading or watching a favorite TV program.

Simple Ways to Enjoy Mint

Mint refreshes your mind and body as well as your surroundings. When you want to bring that freshness into your day, here are a few suggestions:

Sip a cup of mint tea early in the morning.

Chew a sprig of mint to freshen your breath.

Put a sprig of peppermint in your hot chocolate. Yum!

Drop 1 or 2 sprigs of mint in your bottled water. So refreshing and energizing anytime.

Refresh any room in your house with a vase of freshly cut mint.

Add mint leaves to birdbath water. It will keep the water fresh and inviting for your feathered friends.

Wrap a handful of freshly picked mint in cheesecloth. Drop this bundle in your bathwater.

Rose
rosa rugosa

Meet Rose

I am rose, a symbol of love and beauty. For over three thousand years I have been known as the "Queen of Flowers." Queen Cleopatra adored me. Breathe the sweet perfume of my royal flower and you will want to plant at least one rosebush in your yard.

Did you know that John Adams was the first president to plant rose bushes near the white house? George Washington and Thomas Jefferson were also fans of mine.

Most roses grow upright but some of us like to creep or climb. We may grow from three to six feet tall. Our flowers bloom every spring in shades of pink, lavender, yellow, red, orange, or white. Each of my species has its own wonderful scent.

The stems and branches of most rose bushes have thorns. Be careful. If you want to cut some of our blooms for a bouquet, wear a pair of gloves and use garden clippers. You may want your mom or dad to assist you.

Are you thinking about planting your own rose bush? You might choose one that is without thorns. There are several varieties and nurseries sell them.

I love sunshine but do not mind a little shade. Plant me in well-drained soil. I should be pruned every year in late winter.

Did you know?

When playwright William Shakespeare wasn't performing in London, he lived in a quiet town called Stratford-Upon-Avon in England. Today boats and barges still navigate the cold water of the winding Avon river. Shakespeare was inspired by the beautiful gardens and flowers of Stratford, where he was born, and many of his most famous plays and sonnets include flower symbolism, similes and metaphors.

"With sweet musk-roses and with eglantine:
There sleeps Titania sometime of the night,
Lull'd in these flowers with dances and delight."
-A Midsummer Night's Dream

It's a Secret

In early times roses were a symbol of secrecy. A rose would be hung in a room, perhaps over a table. This meant the words spoken by those in the room were to be kept secret.

Native Americans and Roses

American Natives used roses for medicine and decoration. On their wedding day, Native maidens placed roses in their hair. Native people also used rosewater to bathe sore eyes and freshen tired skin. Powder made from the dried petals was placed on fever blisters. When used in this way, rose powder was found to be both soothing and healing.

Petal Pioneers

Use rose petals to flavor tea, punch, honey, and vinegar

Bake them into an apple pie as the pioneer women did

Toss them into a fruit salad

Dip strawberries in rose sugar

Rose-Scented Happiness

Today we grow roses for their beauty and wonderful fragrance. Bowls of dried rose petals, lavender, and cinnamon make a wonderful potpourri. Rose oil, distilled from petals, is used to scent perfumes and soaps. Rose water is another way to scent your home. Use a small spray bottle to mist the air or yourself. Rose water is sold in health food stores and online but you can also make your own.

What is a Rose hip?

Roses are not often used as medicine. However, rose hips are good to use for a sore throat or cold. The rose hip is a small fruit that grows on rosebushes. They are rich in vitamins and minerals, especially vitamin C. Many people like to drink tea made from rose hips when they have a cold. Rose hip honey is delicious and soothing for sore throats.

A Rose Story

Sara believed her abuelita should have been named Rose. Abuelita lived alone in a cozy, two bedroom house. Though the house was small, the backyard was spacious. Abuelita loved to plant her rosebushes there. Twelve bushes, each one a different variety, were planted along the back fence. Five more lined the driveway. Dainty miniature roses decorated the patio and front porch.

In all, abuelita had twenty-four rosebushes and said she'd like to have more. Sara often spied William the robin hopping from bush to bush. He liked to eat the insects that fed on the roses. Abuelita appreciated William's efforts to keep her beautiful roses free from insects. As a thank you, she planted blackberries and raspberries along the back fence. Abuelita knew that William would enjoy the vine-ripened berries. She also placed a birdbath near the berry vines so William could clean his feathers whenever he wished.

William's friend Lady Blossom also liked to eat insects and spiders. The mischievous humming bird would zip around William, her blue-green body shimmering in the sunshine. Sometimes she paused

midair to pose for a photograph. Sara liked to take photos of the tiny bird as she sipped nectar from red bud sage blossoms. William called Blossom his second-in-command and the two of them kept their beady eyes on the roses, watching for insect predators.

Abuelita loved to bring her rose garden indoors. Rose-filled vases could be found in every room. Rose petals were tossed in drawers and cupboards. One day Sara asked, "Abuelita, wouldn't you like to plant other flowers? Don't you ever get tired of roses?"

Abuelita laughed as she handed Sara a pink rose bud to smell.

"Roses lift my spirits, " she said. "They remind me that the world is a beautiful place to be."

That night, Sara slept at her abuelita's house. The sweet perfume of abuelita's roses drifted through her bedroom window the next morning and she leapt out of bed, for once pleased to get up early. She could hear William singing his sweet song. When she stuck her head out of the window, she saw he was deep in conversation with another bird. Their voices echoed around the garden. She wished she could understand them.

"Hi, William!" she called. She pulled her head back and barreled downstairs toward the irresistible scent of hot, freshly baked pan dulce, a sweet Mexican bread. As a special treat, abuelita had baked some of her homemade strawberry jam inside the bread.

After breakfast, abuelita put on her old gardening gloves and said, "Let's gather rose petals." Sara found the basket, and stepped out into the dewy morning air. The sun was gathering its strength as Abuelita showed Sara which roses were ready to drop their petals. Using garden clippers, she cut the older roses and lay them in the basket. Some of the petals fell off by themselves. Sara gently released the rest. The basket was soon filled with a sweet smelling mound of soft, silky petals.

Sara closed her eyes and lowered her face into the petals. She breathed in one of nature's finest perfumes. William puffed out his red chest and pretended he was cleaning his feathers, but he hopped a little closer to the basket when he thought Sara wasn't looking, his little black eyes curious.

Back in the kitchen, Abuelita asked Sara to spread the petals on a drying screen.

"Why?" Sara asked.

"We're going to make rose sugar. The petals must be dry before we add them to the sugar."

The next week passed by all too slowly, but finally Sara returned to Abuelita's house, excited to make rose sugar. The petals had dried.

Abuelita showed her how to use a spice grinder. Sara dropped a handful of dried petals into the bowl of the grinder. As the little machine did its job, all the petals became a sweet-smelling red dust.

Next, Abuelita took a box of Baker's sugar from the cupboard. Baker's sugar had a soft, velvety texture. The grains were finer than regular sugar. She measured one cup into a small bowl.

Then she asked Sara to add a heaping tablespoon of rose dust to the bowl of sugar. As Sara blended the rose dust into the sugar, she wondered how it would taste. Without hesitation, she dipped a moist finger into the bowl. Sugar had never, ever tasted so good!

Sara wanted to dip her finger into the sugar bowl again and again, but Abuelita had another plan. She asked Sara to follow her out to the garden. The garden was filled with lettuce, tomatoes, onions, peppers, bright red strawberries and a furtive William, who wanted to know what interesting thing Sara was doing this time.

Sara and Abuelita filled a basket with the plump, sweet-smelling berries. Back in the kitchen the strawberries were gently rinsed. Soon Sara and her abuelita were dipping garden-ripe berries into the rose sugar. A feeling of pure joy filled Sara. She never imagined strawberries and roses would taste so good together. Later that day Abuelita gave Sara a jar of rose sugar and a basket of freshly picked strawberries to take home. Sara was certain her mom and dad would enjoy this garden treat as much as she did. She left a rose strawberry on William's bird feeder, as a "thank you" for protecting the beautiful roses.

Romantic Rose Water

There are so many fun ways to use rose petals. They are beautiful to use as decorations. They are cooling and can be put in teas and drinks to temper hot summer days. They are also used to make rose water. Mist your face or spray rose water in the rooms of your house. The wonderful scent will bring your garden indoors

You will need:

3 to 4 cups rose petals

1 cup distilled water

1 glass mason jar

8 ounce spray bottle

To make a wonderful rose water mist:

Fill a glass jar with tightly packed rose petals.

Cover the petals with water and put a lid on the jar.

Place it near a sunny window for at least two days.

Use a strainer to remove petals from the scented water.

Store in the refrigerator.

Put it in a spray bottle if you wish to use it as a room spray.

Rose Smoothie

You really can make smoothies out of rose petals! This is an unusually delicious beverage. Rose petals have an affinity for mint, lemon juice, and honey. The first time I enjoyed this refreshing beverage, I walked about my garden with a wide, happy smile. The ingredients for this recipe are simple.

You will need:

1 cup cooled rose petal and mint leaf tea

4 teaspoons fresh lemon juice

3 tablespoons honey

1/2 cup crushed ice

Lemon or lime slices for garnish

To make a delicious rose smoothie:

1. Make rose petal tea by steeping four to five fresh pink or red rose petals with a few fresh mint leaves.

2. Cool and strain the rose petals and mint leaves from the water.

3. Put the tea and honey into the blender along with the other ingredients. Blend and enjoy.

Drink your smoothie fresh. They taste best this way. However, they can be stored in the refrigerator overnight.

Roses for Lunch

There are people who like to walk about their gardens eating rose petals. I am not one of them. However, I do like to make rose petal cream cheese or butter to put inside a sandwich. Some folks also like to add rose petals to green or fruit salads.

To make a sandwich, you will need:

Fresh rose petals

Softened cream cheese or butter

Turkey or other filling

Directions:

1. Chop up the fresh rose petals and stir them into softened cream cheese or butter.

2. Spread the rose butter or cream cheese on bread with thinly sliced turkey, sliced cucumber, or another filling of your choice.

For salads, tear or cut rose petals into small pieces. Toss them into your salad. Lettuce, cucumber celery, onions, and rose petals are tasty with a raspberry vinaigrette salad dressing.

Important Note: Rose petals used in food recipes need to be grown without pesticides.

Smell as Sweet as a Rose

Dried rosebuds provide a soothing bath. The following recipe is a blend of dried rosebuds, lavender, and chamomile.

You will need:

1 part dried rosebuds

1 part dried chamomile

1 part dried lavender flowers

Relax in your rose bath, after you:

1. Mix together the dried flowers. Store in a glass jar.

2. To make a bath sachet, cut a piece of cotton fabric into an 8-inch square.

3. Fill the center of the fabric with a handful of the rose bath recipe.

4. Lift the edges and close with a small rubber band. A piece of ribbon or raffia can be tied around the rubber band for decoration.

5. Drop the sachet into a tub of very warm water. Squeeze the wet sachet several times to release a healing herbal tea into your bath.

6. When the water has cooled a little, climb in and enjoy!

Magic Away Musty Smells

As early as the 16th century, rose sweet bags were used to scent linen and hang on the arms of wing back chairs. They were also tucked inside drawers to remove musty smells.

Sweet, sweet ingredients:

8 teaspoons dried roses

2 teaspoons lavender

2 teaspoons marjoram

1 inch of crushed cinnamon stick

4 cloves

1 pinch rosemary

1 crushed bay leaf

Sweet bag assembly:

1. Mix all of the herbs and spices together.

2. Store in a covered jar for two to three days (this requires a little patience, but it will be worth it!)

3. To make a sweet bag, cut a piece of fabric into an eight-inch square.

4. Fill the center of the square with a handful of the herbs and spices.

5. Lift the edges and tie closed with a piece of ribbon.

6. Use your sweet bag to scent your drawers, closet, towels, or sheets. Maybe you can think of other ways to use your sweet bag.

Note: **The sweet bag will last four to five months or longer.**

A Very Thorny History

Silence of the Roses

The ancient Romans liked to wear rose necklaces. If they knew a secret, they would say it was: "sub rosa," a Latin idiom meaning "under the rose."

Roses were an ancient symbol of silence and secrecy. At dinner parties, wealthy Romans decorated their ceiling with roses, to remind the guests that anything said at the party was confidential.

The Wildest Emperor of Them All

Emperor Nero used roses to liven up his parties. He installed holes in the ceilings of his Domus Aurea (Golden House) through which slaves sprinkled rose petals and perfume on his honored guests while they dined. His invention wasn't perfect. One guest supposedly suffocated under an avalanche of rose petals!

Ancient Sayings Die Hard

The U.S. military still uses the term "sub rosa" in military courts and in reference to covert operations.

Graduation Day

Congratulations! You are now a Junior Herbalist! I hope your new herb garden is flourishing, and you've had a lot of fun making the recipes in this book.

The Crestwood Elementary Herb Garden Club concludes for the year each May. Our last meeting of the school year is graduation day. Students are awarded a Junior Herbalist Certificate if they attended weekly meetings and completed their herb garden journal. The certificate recognizes students for the herbs they have learned to identify, grow, and use throughout the year.

At the end of this book, you will find your very own Junior Herbalist Certificate. You can write your name on it and print it out. Stick it to your fridge with a magnet, pin it on your bedroom wall, or post a photo online to share with your friends. If you find William the robin online at www.timelessherbaltraditions.com, he will congratulate you personally. We both love to hear about our readers' experiences with this book, and all the great recipes you have made. Follow us online to hear about herb garden club news and competitions.

At Crestwood Elementary, we celebrate our year together with generous servings of green chile chicken enchiladas prepared with fresh thyme from the garden. Laughter fills the library as we watch a slideshow of us enjoying Wednesday afternoons with the herbs and each other.

So many times students have asked to take their journals home. Now, at last, the day has come. They are proud to claim their colorful notebooks filled with a collection of herbal drawings, notes, and recipes.

Receiving this award and the title, Jr. Herbalist, is an honor. It also carries responsibility. As we say our final goodbyes for the year, I remind students to use their skill and knowledge as Jr. Herbalists to teach others. Walk the garden with a friend. Give them a chocolate mint leaf to nibble. Let them touch a soft silky rose petal and sniff the bright uplifting scent of a lemon balm leaf. Ask them to look for William who may be hopping from bush to bush, or singing in the trees.

Throughout the year students are encouraged to grow an herb garden in their backyard or in pots on the back porch. Many have transplanted sprouts from the school garden to their home gardens. When the herbs are close by they can easily make recipes from their journals for family and friends to enjoy.

I've enjoyed the garden with my students for many years and sometimes I come across former students. They almost always asked, "Is the garden still there?" I am pleased to tell them it is and that they are welcome to come back for a visit.

One young lady told me she created a potted herb garden outside her dorm window when she went away to college. "College can be stressful," she said. "When I look through the window and see all the herbs reaching for the sun, I know my day is going to be good one."

With love from the Herb Garden Club,
Kathy, and William the Robin

A distinguished member of the

Crestwood Herb Garden Club

---

is recognized as a

Junior Herbalist

For Learning to Identify and Use the Herbs Lavender, Lemon Balm, Rosemary, Chamomile, Thyme, Mint, and Rose.

Recipes to Relish!

How many recipes in this book can you make? Check them off the list and take photos of your marvelous creations. Post your mouthwatering or refreshing photos online, or make an art gallery on your bedroom wall or your fridge.

Lavender Recipes

☐ Lavender Sniffies

☐ Lavender Dream Pillows

☐ Lavender Sprinkling Sugar

☐ Lavender Cookies

☐ Lavender White Cake

☐ Lavender Doggy Powder

☐ Lavender Room Scent

Lemon Balm Recipes

☐ Lemon Balm Lemonade

☐ Lemon Balm Ice Cubes

☐ Green Salad with Lemon Balm

☐ Lemon Balm Longevity Tea

☐ Scented Book Pages

☐ Shoe Freshening

☐ Lemon Balm Lavender Bath Bag

Rosemary Recipes

☐ Rosemary Gingerbread Cookies

☐ Rosemary Salt

☐ Friendship Bouquet

☐ Rosemary Bath

☐ Winter Holiday Potpourri

Chamomile Recipes

☐ Mark's Chamomile Garden Tea

☐ Chamomile Iced Tea with Apple Juice

☐ Chamomile Smoothie

☐ Cooling Chamomile Spritzer

☐ Closet Sachets

Recipes to Relish!

Have you made every single recipe? If you have, you can unlock a secret page at our website. Go to www.timelessherbaltraditions.com/william to unlock a secret herb recipe and a story about William.

Thyme Recipes
- ☐ Andrew's Thyme Honey
- ☐ Herb Butter with Thyme
- ☐ Green Chile Thyme Enchiladas
- ☐ Apple Thyme Jelly
- ☐ Thyme Herbal Bath Bags

Mint Recipes
- ☐ Teapot Mint Tea
- ☐ Sunshine Mint Tea
- ☐ Minty Cucumber Salad
- ☐ Peppermint Brownies
- ☐ Refresh Mint

Rose Recipes
- ☐ Rose Sugar
- ☐ Romantic Rose Water
- ☐ Rose Smoothie
- ☐ Roses for Lunch (Rose Sandwich)
- ☐ Rose Bath
- ☐ Rose Sweet Bag

Thank You

Jim Sullivan, former principal of Crestwood School, for encouraging me to start an herb garden club. Once the weekly meetings began, the needed resources were always made available.

Dedi Somavia, Crestwood's School's current principal. Your enthusiastic support of the herb garden club is appreciated.

Susan Haynes, master gardener, for volunteering your time on Wednesday afternoons. You are always there to assist with activities and make sure club meetings run smoothly.

Laura Mevinne, for assisting with the garden club when your schedule permits.

Olivia Aguigam, my former student. You attended garden club on Wednesday afternoons to help younger students with their journals and crafts.

Cheryl Aguigam, Olivia's mother. From day one you were always there on Wednesdays to lend your support. A special thanks for creating the DVD's we all enjoyed on graduation day.

Granddaughters(all four of you) for working with your grandmother to create and sample new herbal recipes. Your feedback was invaluable.

Daughter Lindsay. You created a fine Jr. Herbalist certificate.

Sarah Garcia, you created a wonderful pen and ink drawing of our school herb garden.

Joey Gist, my wonderful editor. You encouraged me to be more playful and authentic as a writer. You were also instrumental in the creation of William. Both William and I are grateful.

Nyssa Shaw, for your inspired illustrations that bring life and meaning to the printed word. You also did a brilliant job with the layout.

Christina Lynch, for taking the time to do one last edit before this book made its way to the printers.

Stan Stevens, my husband. You communicate so easily with the green folks and you have helped me to do the same. Working side by side with you in the garden is one of my favorite things to do. Thanks also for patiently reading and rereading the herb stories. Your comments have been invaluable.

Bibliography

Ferry-Swanson, Kate. Chamomile. Boston, Massachusetts: Tuttle Publishing, 2000.

Gray, Linda. *Herbs and Spices*. New York: Skyhouse Publishing, 2011.

Kowalchik, Claire. *Rodale's Illustrated Encyclopedia of Herbs*. Emmaus, Pennsylvania: Rodale Press, Inc. 1987.

Hartung, Tammi. *Homegrown Herbs*. Massachusetts, Story Publishing, 2011.

Houdret, Jessica. *Growing Herbs*. London: Arness Publishing, 2004.

Hylton, William. *The Rodale Herb Book*. Emmaus, Pennsylvania: Rodale Press, Inc., 1987.

Lovejoy, Sharon. *Roots, Shoots, Buckets and Boots*. New York: Workman Publishing, 1999.

Louv, Richard. *Last Child in the Woods*. Chapel Hill, North Carolina: Algonquin Books of Chapel Hill, 2008.

Shipley, Sharon. *The Lavender Cookbook*. Philadelphia, Pennsylvania: Running Press Book Publishers, 2004.

Sinclair Rohde, Eleanour. *Rose Recipes from Olden Times*. New York: Press, 1978.

Smith, Miranda. Your Backyard Herb Garden. Rodale Press, 1997.

Zak, Victoria. The Magic Teaspoon. New York, New York: Penguin Group, 2006.